CADD PRIMER

A general guide to Computer Aided Design and Drafting – CADD, CAD

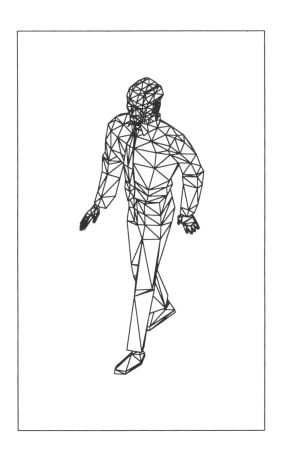

Mailmax Publishing
New York

CADD PRIMER
A general guide to Computer Aided Design and Drafting – CADD, CAD

© 1999 MailMax Publishing, New York

All rights reserved.

MailMax Publishing, 43-15 Judge St., Suite 1R, Flushing, New York 11373.
Voice and fax: 1(914) 614-3269, Web site: http://www.caddprimer.com
E-mail: mailmax@caddprimer.com

Publisher's Cataloging-in-Publication
(Provided by Quality Books, Inc.)

    Duggal, Vijay.
      CADD primer : a general guide to computer aided design and drafting : CADD, CAD / Vijay Duggal. -- 1st ed.

      p. cm.
      Includes bibliographical references and index.
      LCCN: 99-74579
      ISBN: 0-9629165-2-8 (hbk.)
      ISBN: 0-9629165-9-5 (pbk.)

      1. Computer-aided design. 2. Computer graphics.
    I. Title.

TA345.D84 2000   620'.0042'0285
                        QBI99-500469
                        MARC

Preface

Welcome to the world of **C**omputer **A**ided **D**esign and **D**rafting (CADD). *CADD PRIMER* is designed to teach you all the skills necessary to learn CADD in a successful and professional manner. It assumes that you have very little experience with computers; however, you are familiar with basic geometry and the concept of drawing.

CADD software is commonly used for drafting architectural and engineering drawings and for making technical illustrations of any kind. If you are a professional associated with design or drafting or would just like to widen your knowledge about CADD applications, then *CADD PRIMER* is for you.

CADD enables you to prepare fast and accurate drawings. It provides flexibility to change drawings with minimal effort. In recent years, many professionals have switched to CADD to enjoy the benefits of this precise and creative tool. Today, many educational institutions include CADD as part of their academic curriculum. As a result, CADD knowledge has become very important to all professionals involved in the field of design and drafting.

There are a variety of systems and programs available in the CADD industry and new programs are frequently introduced. It has become very confusing to select a system and learn all the applications and techniques of CADD. Design and operation of CADD programs differ from system to system, and time spent in learning one system may not prove very useful on another.

CADD PRIMER does not focus on a specific CADD program. It provides general information that is applicable to all the leading CADD programs, such as AutoCAD, MicroStation and Cadkey. *CADD PRIMER* can give you a head start in learning CADD, regardless of whatever CADD program you may have to use.

Who can benefit from CADD PRIMER:
● Students associated with drawing.
● Design and drafting professionals who would like to get a quick overview of CADD.
● A novice or scholar who always wondered how the drawings are created using a computer!

Important note:
CADD PRIMER is not a "how-to" book. Although it uses examples from leading CADD programs, they are intended to illustrate general principles only.
CADD PRIMER is a beginner's reference book on CADD.

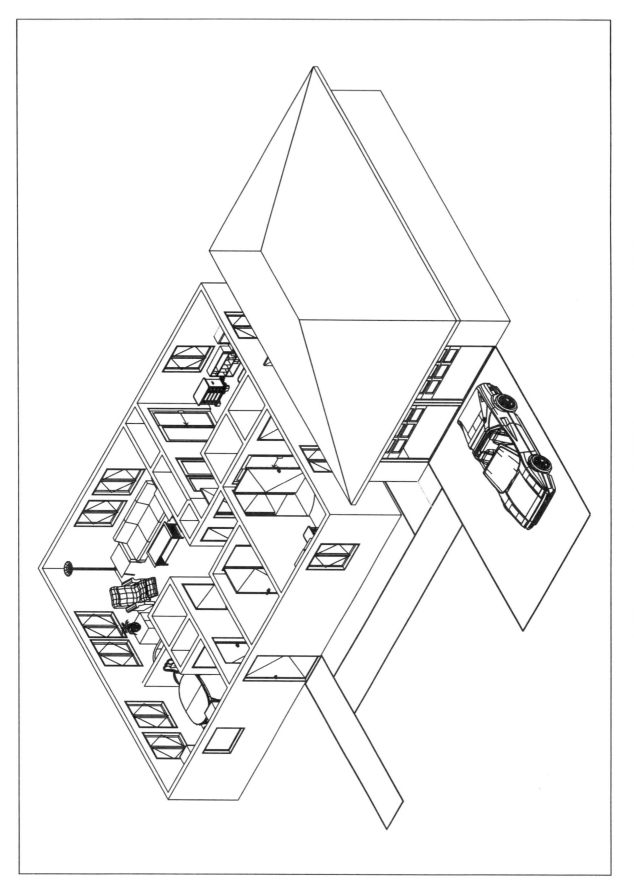

An example 3D drawing created using CADD: Image courtesy Eaglepoint Software.

An example drawing created using CADD. Courtesy Peter Dahms.

Author:

Vijay Duggal:

Architect with extensive experience using CADD, New York.

Member:

American Design Drafting Association (ADDA)

US National CAD Standard committee

CAD Society

Technical Editors:

Al Zoli

Sella Rush

Reviewers and Contributors:

Prof. Eden Muir: CAD department, Columbia University

Mr. Robert Mertz: CAD class, New York Institute of Technology

Prof. Bruice M. Coleman: CAD class, Syracuse University

Dr. Jens Pohl: CAD Research Center, California Polytechnic State University

Mr. Emille Griffing: American Design Drafting Association

Mr. David Byrnes: CAD systems magazine

Mr. Richard Todd: CAD class, New York University

Mr. James Wilson: CADD/GIS Technology Center, US Department of Defense

Acknowledgments:

Editors, reviewers and contributors

Friends and family

Hardware and software vendors listed in this book

Table of Contents

Table of Contents

Table of Contents

Table of Contents

Introduction

Contents

3D CADD renderings created using SoftCAD: Images courtesy SoftCAD International.

Introduction

Key Terms in this Chapter

Term	Description
Attributes	Descriptions of electronic drawing elements.
CAD	An acronym for Computer Aided Design. It synonymously used for Computer Aided Drafting.
CADD	An acronym for Computer Aided Design & Drafting.
CADD system	A computer system that enables you to perform drawing and design tasks.
CAFM	An acronym for Computer Aided Facility Management
CAE	An acronym for Computer Aided Engineering
CAM	An acronym for Computer Aided Manufacturing
Command	A single instruction issued by the user to complete a task on the computer.
Database	A stored collection of data that can be retrieved and organized in different ways.
Function	A task in a program that can be completed by issuing a set of commands through the program.
Menu	A collection of functions or commands that are displayed on the screen. You can make selections from the menu with a pointing device such as a mouse.
Parametric design	A computer capability that links graphics on the screen with automated calculations and vice versa.

What is CADD?

When we think of Computer Aided Design and Drafting (CADD), certain questions arise that we never think of while working on the drawing board. We do not use the essential drawing board tools: paper, pencil, T-square, compass, eraser or scale, yet still have to design or make a drawing. When even one of these tools is missing we know how aggravating it can be. With CADD we don't need even one of them!

CADD is an electronic tool that enables you to make quick and accurate drawings with the use of a computer. Unlike the traditional methods of making drawings on a drawing board, with CADD you can sit back in an easy chair and create wonderful drawings just by clicking the buttons of a keyboard. Moreover, drawings created with CADD have a number of advantages over drawings created on a drawing board. CADD drawings are neat, clean and highly presentable. Electronic drawings can be modified quite easily and can be presented in a variety of formats.

A decade ago, CADD was used only for specific engineering applications that required high precision. Due to CADD's high price, only a few professionals could afford it. In recent years, however, computer prices have decreased significantly and more and more professionals are taking advantage of CADD.

There are hundreds of CADD programs available in the CADD industry today. Some are intended for general drawing work while others are focused on specific engineering applications. There are programs that enable you to do 2D drawings, 3D drawings, renderings, shadings, engineering calculations, space planning, structural design, piping layouts, plant design, project management, etc. There is a CADD program for virtually every engineering discipline you can think of.

CADD is primarily intended for single-line drafting. It has very limited capabilities to create artistic impressions. However, CADD's 3D and rendering features are fascinating. You can create a 3D model of an object and view it from any angle. With proper shading and rendering, it can be made to look picture perfect!

What to Expect from CADD

You can do amazing things with CADD that you never thought possible while creating drawings with a pen or pencil. The following are some of the important capabilities that make CADD a powerful tool:

- Presentations
- Flexibility in editing
- Units & accuracy levels
- Storage and access for drawings
- Sharing CADD drawings
- Project reporting
- Engineering analysis
- Computer Aided Manufacturing (CAM)
- Design
- Add-on programs

Presentations

You can create fine drawings with hundreds of colors, line types, hatch patterns, presentation symbols, text styles, etc. Even if you don't like something about your presentation after you have finished it, you can instantly change it. It takes only a few simple steps to change the text style, color or line type and you can print a fresh copy of the drawing every time. This kind of luxury is available only when working with CADD.

There are a number of ready-made presentation symbols and hatch patterns available in CADD that can be used to enhance the look of drawings. For example, a site planner can instantly add tree symbols, shrubs, pathways, human figures, and other landscape elements to create a site plan. Similarly, an architect can use ready-made symbols of doors, windows, furniture, etc., to make a presentation.

In addition to preparing impressive presentations on paper, you can use CADD to make on-screen presentations. You can plug your computer into a projector and present your ideas on-screen. Advanced CADD programs allow you to created animated images as well. You can illustrate how a building would appear while walking through it, or how a machine assembly will operate when different machine parts move.

Flexibility in Editing

CADD provides the flexibility to make quick alterations to drawings. You can erase any portion of a drawing with pinpoint accuracy. It takes only seconds to do a job that could take hours on a drawing board. In many cases, you do not even have to erase to make the change. You can rearrange the existing components of the drawing to fit the new shape. This enables you to analyze design options with minimal effort.

The following are some of the editing capabilities of CADD:

- Move or copy drawing elements
- Enlarge or reduce parts of a drawing
- Add one drawing to another
- Stretch a drawing to fit new dimensions
- Make multiple copies of a drawing element
- Change the size, style and fonts of text
- Change units of measure of dimensions

Units & Accuracy Levels

CADD allows you work with great accuracy. If you need to create highly accurate geometrical shapes, CADD is the answer. It can help avoid time-consuming mathematical calculations.

You can work with different units of measure, such as architectural units, engineering units, scientific units and surveyor's units. These units can be represented in various formats commonly used by professionals.

Example: When working with engineering units, you can specify whether all the dimensions should be represented in inches, feet-inches, centimeters, or meters. Similarly, you can choose angular units of measurement such as decimal degrees, minutes, seconds or radians.

You can set an extremely high accuracy for the units of measurement. You can work with as high precision as $1/1000^{th}$ of an inch! However, such accuracy is seldom required; you will often need to set it to a lesser accuracy to avoid unnecessary fractions.

In general, when you need to work on a large scale drawing such as a plan of a township, you may want to set a lesser degree of accuracy, say 1'-0". The computer will round off all the measurements to the next foot and you won't see any fractions less than a foot. When you need to work on a minute detail, you can set a higher degree of accuracy such as $1/8^{th}$ or $1/64^{th}$ of an inch.

Storage and Access of Drawings

It is quick and convenient to organize for a CADD drawing in the computer. You can have thousands of drawings on a computer's hard disk and can open any one of them within seconds.

A computer's electronic filing system has the following advantages over the traditional filing system:

- It enables you to create a highly organized environment
- It contributes to large savings in working space
- An electronic drawing never gets old and faded. Any time you need a drawing, you can print a new copy from disks.

Sharing CADD Drawings

The electronic drawings can be shared by a number of users, allowing them to coordinate their tasks and work as a team. This is accomplished by connecting different computers via a network.

Example: In a building project, different professionals such as architects, engineers and construction managers can use the same electronic drawings to coordinate building services. If a change is made to the drawings, this information becomes available to all the team members instantly.

With the use of modems and the Internet, it has become far easier to share information. Professionals located in different cities can instantly send electronic drawings via telephone lines.

You can publish your drawings on the Internet for anyone to see. Most CADD programs include special functions that allow you to export drawings in a format that can be viewed on the Internet.

Project Reporting

The computer can be used to prepare project reports such as records of areas, quantities and cost estimates. Using the database capabilities of CADD, you can link specific non-graphic information (such as text or value) with the graphic elements of the drawing. The non-graphic information is stored in a database and can be used to prepare reports.

Example: An architect can attach text attributes associated with the symbols of doors and windows in a drawing. The attributes can describe the size of the door, material, hardware, cost, etc. Later on the computer can automatically prepare a door schedule listing all the doors and windows in the drawing!

The non-graphic information is directly linked with the graphics on the screen. When a change is made to the drawing, the values in the reports are updated automatically. This provides a useful means to manage large projects from design through project completion.

There is a special category of software called Computer Aided Facility Management (CAFM) designed for project management. These programs can import information from CADD drawings and allow you to add attributes to drawing elements to build a database. The database can be used to prepare project reports in a number of formats.

See Chapter 10 "CADD Industry Resources" for a list of computer aided facility management software.

Engineering Analysis

CADD drawings can be used to perform specific engineering analysis. There is a separate category of programs called Computer Aided Engineering (CAE) that can use CADD drawings for engineering analysis.

Example: A structural engineer can use a CAE program to test the design of structural components in different conditions. The engineer can instantly analyze the impact on structural members when a different load is applied to the structure or the spacing between the members is changed. Similarly, there are programs for mechanical engineers to test machine assemblies. The mechanical engineer can create a prototype electronic model and test it without building a physical model.

The advanced engineering programs even provide the ability to link calculations with the geometry on the screen. This capability is known as "parametric design" that allows the computer to automatically update the graphics when the associated calculations are changed and vice versa.

Computer Aided Manufacturing (CAM)

CADD extends its power to yet another branch of engineering called Computer Aided Manufacturing (CAM). CAM is a common method of manufacturing used by large corporations. CADD and manufacturing programs are often integrated into one system called CAD-CAM. These systems import CADD drawings into CAM programs to automate the manufacturing process.

Example: An engineer can draw a machine part using CADD. The CADD drawing is brought into a computer aided engineering (CAE) program for engineering analysis. When the design is finalized, the drawing is brought into a CAD-CAM system that uses numerical data from the CADD drawing for actual manufacturing.

Design

CADD provides a convenient means to create designs for almost every engineering discipline. It can be used for architectural design, landscape design, interior design, civil and surveying, mechanical design, electrical engineering, plant design, industrial design, duct design, electronic circuit design, plumbing design, textile design and product design.

CADD's drafting capabilities provide ample means to create a design scheme. You can create designs with great accuracy and have the flexibility to easily edit them. This allows you to quickly prepare design alternatives.

In addition to the drafting capabilities of CADD, there are special programs that can analyze designs or even create new ones. These programs use artificial intelligence to "think" and make design decisions.

The design capabilities of CADD are available only in advanced CADD programs. There are only a few such programs available. Design programs are usually not generic. They often need to be custom-written to accomplish a specific task. See Chapter 9 "Maximizing CADD" for discussion on design programs.

Add-on Programs

There are a number of separate programs available that can enhance the power of CADD. The add-on programs work as an extension of CADD to accomplish specific tasks. Today, there are hundreds of add-on programs available for popular CADD programs.

An architectural add-on program can allow you to instantly draw symbols of doors, windows, kitchens, bathrooms, staircases, etc. A shading and rendering program can be used to enhance the look of 3D images. A plumbing design program includes special functions to draw pipes, drains and plumbing joints. A civil engineering program includes special features to work with contours and land development; the list goes on and on.

Most manufacturers market CADD programs in separate modules. They sell a basic drafting module for a certain price with the options to add on other modules. There are a number of add-on programs available from independent vendors as well.

A Look at the CADD Industry

There are hundreds of CADD programs available in the CADD industry today. Most of them are simply drafting programs, while some offer certain engineering analysis, design or database capabilities. Some programs are more elaborate than others. You can purchase a CADD program with just the basic drawing capabilities for as little as $200. These are called low-end programs and are commonly used for general drawing work.

Another category of software is mid-range. This category offers advanced drafting techniques such as layers, 3D, basic database capabilities, advanced dimensioning and many automated drawing features. Architecture and engineering design firms commonly use mid-range software. About 80% of all the CADD programs fall into this category and there is immense competition in this market. Their prices vary significantly.

There are a few advanced CADD programs available, which are commonly used by large corporations for manufacturing. These programs include integrated features such as solid modeling, engineering analysis, design, database and project management. These are called high-end programs. Most of the time they are customized to meet the specific requirements of the corporation. These programs are priced quite high.

Note: It's often hard to determine whether a program is low-end, mid-range or high-end. Low-end programs claim to be mid-range, while mid-range programs claim to be high-end.

Certain CADD programs have gained popularity among groups of professionals due to their unique characteristics. For example, AutoCAD has gained popularity among architects and other engineering trades associated with building construction. Microstation and Datacad are also quite well known in this industry. Allplan, ArchiCAD and Arris are popular architectural software programs in Europe. Pro-engineer has the largest market share in the mechanical engineering CADD market. Cadkey, CADDS, VELLUM and MicroCADAM are also quite popular in the mechanical market. Archibus, Drawbase and Aperture are specifically designed for facility management. MiniCAD and PowerCAD are favorites among Macintosh brand computer users. TurboCAD and DesignCAD are affordable industrial design programs. 3D studio, Form-Z and Lightscape are well-known rendering software. For more information, see Chapter 10 "CADD Industry Resources."

Important Tip:

Additional information about the CADD industry can be obtained by logging on to a web site dedicated to this book http://www.caddprimer.com, which contains hundreds of links to web sites associated with the CADD industry.

The Focus of this Book

With so many CADD programs available, it is impossible to learn each one. Most programs have similar drawing capabilities, but the exact procedures are quite different. You may be an expert on one program and yet not know much about another. This is because different CADD programs use different terminology and procedures to accomplish the same tasks. It may take you quite some time to learn the intricacies of a particular CADD program.

CADD PRIMER is designed to give you a head start in learning CADD regardless of any program you may have to use. It describes the general principles and applications of CADD that are applicable to most of the programs. Its objective is to familiarize you with all the aspects of working with CADD. Once you understand what individual functions do and which functions to use where, you can apply this knowledge to any CADD program.

The following are the main objectives of CADD PRIMER:

- To present an overview of CADD and describe its applications in different fields.

- To describe common terms associated with CADD hardware and software.

- To outline the basic principles associated with CADD and to demonstrate common drafting techniques and shortcuts used by professionals.

- To introduce the advanced capabilities of CADD and how they can be used to increase productivity.

- To provide information about the CADD industry resources.

How to Use *CADD PRIMER*

CADD PRIMER is a reference book. The examples in this book are illustrated in a generic way, because our objective is not to focus on a specific program. The examples used in this book are intended to give you an idea of how CADD works and what it can do for you. To learn about a specific program, you will have to obtain literature specific to that program.

A look inside *CADD PRIMER...*

Chapter	Description
Chapter 1: *CADD Hardware and Software*	Gives an overview of CADD hardware and describes the terminology associated with the equipment. Presents an overview of CADD functions and describes their role in CADD and how they are organized in various menus. Teaches you how to communicate with CADD through different means of data entry.

Chapter	Description
Chapter 2: *CADD Basics*	Instructs you on the basic drawing concepts of CADD. You will start with a simple drawing exercise. Explains the essential features of CADD, such as how to enter distances using different coordinate methods. You will learn how to use Absolute, Relative and Polar coordinates. Presents guidelines on setting up a prototype CADD drawing. You will learn how to save and manage CADD drawings.
Chapter 3: *The Drawing Tools*	Gives you a closer look at all the drawing capabilities of CADD. You will learn different methods for drawing lines, arcs, polylines, text, dimensions, etc.
Chapter 4: *View Displays*	Describes how View-Display functions are used to display different views of a drawing. You will learn how to zoom in on portions of the drawing and how to save and restore selected views.
Chapter 5: *The Edit Functions*	Describes the application of CADD's edit functions. You will learn a number of shortcut methods to fix errors. You will also learn how easy it is to make changes by using the erase, copy and move functions. Includes a number of exercises to illustrate functions.
Chapter 6: *Working with Layers*	Discusses the use of layers in CADD drawings. This is a commonly used technique that enables you to organize your drawings better by grouping information on specific layers.
Chapter 7: *Introduction to 3D*	Gives an overview of 3D functions of CADD. You will learn basic 3D drawing techniques. Describes how to make isometrics and perspectives, enter 3D coordinates, and display 3D views from different angles.
Chapter 8: *Printing and Plotting*	Describes CADD's plotting and printing procedures. You will learn how to print the same drawing with a number of variations. Includes a discussion on plotting and printing machines.
Chapter 9: *Maximizing CADD*	Presents an outline of advanced features of CADD, such as the use of attributes to make project reports, the use of macros to do automated tasks, applications of design and database, and how CADD works in an integrated environment with other programs.
Chapter 10: *CADD Industry Resources*	Presents an outline of important features offered by leading CADD programs and the guidelines to choose a CADD system. Includes a helpful CADD directory listing the leading CADD programs and important resources on the Internet.

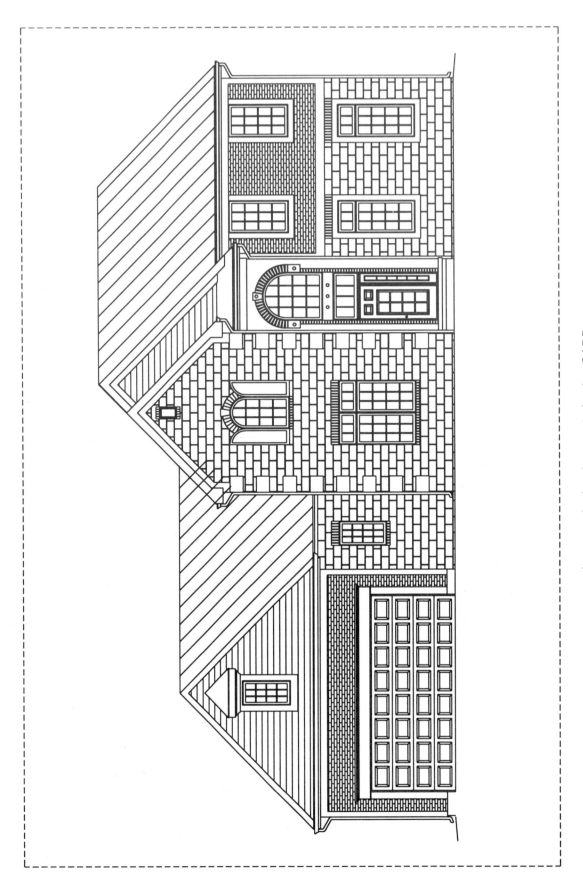

An example drawing created using CADD.

CADD Hardware and Software

1

Contents

An example of a PC based computer system using CADD software.

CADD Hardware and Software

Contents

About this Chapter

This chapter provides a general overview of CADD hardware and software. There are three main topics in this chapter:

- *CADD Hardware*
- *CADD Software*
- *CADD User Interface*

CADD Hardware describes the physical components of a CADD system such as system unit, memory and hard disk. It introduces the requirements and specifications necessary for CADD equipment.

Note: If you are familiar with computers, you may want to browse through the CADD Hardware topic to re-familiarize yourself with information referred to in later chapters. If you are unfamiliar with computers, you should read the entire topic before proceeding.

CADD Software describes the main functions of a CADD program, such as drawing, editing, data output, system control, data storage and management and other special features.

CADD User Interface describes how to interact with CADD by various means of data entry. You will learn how commands are entered using the menus, keyboard, toolbars, etc.

Key Terms in this Chapter

Term	Definition
Bit, byte, megabyte (MB), gigabyte (GB)	A bit is the smallest unit of electronic memory. The second smallest unit of memory is a byte, which contains 8 bits. One megabyte contains one million bytes. 1000 megabytes make one gigabyte.
Data exchange format (DXF)	A standard format used to exchange electronic drawings between different CADD programs.
Digitizer	An electronic data input device.
Dots per inch (dpi)	A specification of printers and plotters that determines how accurately they can print.
Dot-pitch	The distance between the picture elements (pixels) on the screen.
Graphical user interface (GUI)	An environment established by the program that uses graphic clues to help the user communicate with the computer.
Hardware	The physical components of a computer.
Mainframe system	Large computer that processes data at very fast speeds and has a lot of memory. Used by large organizations.
Megahertz (MHz)	The speed of data processing. The speed of one million cycles per second is called 1 MHz.
Minicomputer	Smaller version of the mainframe system. Also used by large organizations.
PC	Personal computer, also know as a microcomputer.
Resolution	The sharpness of the image on the screen.
Server	A computer dedicated to running the network program, with computers connected via a network.
Software	The programs that run on the computer.
Workstation	A complete computer system.

Hardware and Software Overview

There are two parts of a computer system, hardware and software, and a CADD system is no exception. Computer hardware is the physical components of the computer such as system unit, monitor and plotter. Computer software is the program that determines the application of a system.

There are three main categories of computers with respect to hardware:

- Mainframe
- Minicomputer
- Microcomputers, for example personal computers (PCs)

Mainframe computers have a lot of data processing power and their size is quite big. A single mainframe computer performs all the data processing and is accessed via terminals connected to it. Minicomputers are smaller versions of mainframe computers. Microcomputers (PCs) are the desktop or laptop computers of today and are used for individual computing needs.

There are two main categories of computer software:

- System software
- Application program

The system software manages the internal operations of the computer. An important part of the system software is called the operating system (OS). The operating system acts as a platform to run application programs such as CADD. The application program must be compatible with the operating system.

There are a number of operating systems available for different categories of computers; the following are notable to mention:

Operating System	Description
Microsoft Windows	The leading operating system of today commonly used in Intel and IBM-based PCs
MS DOS, PC DOS	The popular operating system of 1980's commonly used in IBM and IBM-compatible PC computers
MAC-OS	Exclusively used in Apple Macintosh brand computers
UNIX	Commonly used in mainframe and minicomputers. There are a number of variations of UNIX available that can be used for different categories of computers including PC's.

Notes:

- CADD programs are available for almost every category of computer. A basic understanding of the operating system is important while working on a computer.

- If you are to select a CADD system, the first step is to select an application program (software) that meets your requirements. After the program is selected, the next step is to select the hardware that can run the program. Keep in mind that there are complete systems available that include both compatible hardware and software.

CADD Hardware

The following are the main hardware components of CADD:

- System unit
  - ➤ Central processing unit
  - ➤ Memory
  - ➤ Hard disk, floppy disk, CD-ROM
- External storage devices
- Monitor
- Printers and plotters
- Keyboard
- Digitizer, puck and mouse

Fig. 1.1: An example of a PC based computer system using CADD software.

System Unit

The system unit is the computer that is used for all data processing. The main components of the system units are the central processing unit (CPU) and memory. In mainframe and minicomputers CPU and memory are usually separate compartments that house thousands of devices. In today's PCs, however, they all fit in a small box commonly known as a desktop computer. Most desktop computers today come equipped with a hard disk, floppy disk drive and CD ROM. Let's have a look at the components of a system unit:

- ➤ Central processing unit
- ➤ Memory
- ➤ Hard disk, floppy disk, CD-ROM

Central Processing Unit (CPU)

The main component that determines the performance of a computer is the central processing unit (CPU). It is also called microprocessor in personal computers. CADD programs require a powerful CPU/microprocessor in order to function properly. In the past, CADD programs could run on mainframe or minicomputers only. Today, however, they can run on PCs.

In today's PC market, computers are generally classified by the kind of microprocessor they use. Major classifications are based on leading brand names, such as Intel, IBM or Apple Macintosh. New microprocessor chips are constantly being developed. A powerful microprocessor is very important to a computer intended to run CADD programs.

Memory

A computer needs memory to process instructions and to display information on the screen. This memory is called random access memory (RAM) because the CPU can access any portion of it at random. RAM is the working place of the computer. Once a computer is started, a program is loaded into the main memory (RAM) of the computer. Whenever a command is issued, the CPU instantly processes that instruction using the RAM.

RAM, therefore, is a major factor in the performance of a computer. CADD programs require that complex graphics be displayed within seconds. Most professional CADD programs require 32 to 64 megabytes (MB) of RAM; however, the more the better. RAM can be easily added to a computer by adding memory chips to the system unit, but there are limitations on the amount of memory a computer can support.

RAM is a temporary storage medium. If the power is disconnected, all the contents supported by this memory are lost. To save information permanently, it must be saved to a computer's hard disk or other data storage device.

Hard Disk, Floppy Disk, CD-ROM

The major storage device for storing electronic information is the hard disk. It is the fastest and most reliable means for storing electronic information. Almost all programs require the use of a hard disk. The hard disk is used to store programs as well as drawings. The hard disk memory is also used in other computer operations.

Hard disks are available in various capacities, from hundreds to thousands of megabytes. Most professional CADD programs require about 100MB of disk space to store and run the program. You will need additional disk space depending upon how many other programs and drawings you plan to store. You will also need space to maintain backup copies of the drawings.

Example: An average engineering drawing takes up about .5 to 1MB of disk space. However, it all depends how many drawing elements are created in a drawing. All the diagrams created in this book used only about 3MB of disk space, all the text used about 1MB.

Floppy disks are commonly used to store data in a portable format. Floppy disks provide a convenient way to move data from one place to another. However, they store only about 1.4MB of data.

CD-ROM drives have become an essential part of today's PCs. Most of the programs now are supplied on compact disks (CDs). You can play a CD in the CD-ROM drive to install programs, to listen to music or to watch a video. Recordable CD-ROMs are also available and can be used to store large amounts of data.

External Storage Devices

There are a number of external storage devices available such as magnetic tapes, zip drives and removable hard disks. They are commonly used to keep backup copies of electronic files for safekeeping.

Magnetic tapes are quite common for storing large volumes of data. A magnetic tape that looks like a small videocassette can store thousands of megabytes of data. However, they are quite slow and require a lot of time to store or retrieve data.

Zip drives were introduced recently; they use zip disks to store data. A zip disk is like an upgraded version of a floppy disk that can store 100MB or more of data. They are particularly helpful if you plan to use CADD or other graphic programs that generate quite big data files. You can store an entire project on one zip disk that could take 50 or more floppy disks.

Another new option for data storage is the removable hard disk. You can remove the entire hard disk from your computer and use it on another computer. This approach is commonly used when you need to work on different computers and you want the same information to be available instantly.

The Monitor

The monitor is the computer screen and is used to display information. A good monitor is very important for CADD in order to display fine graphics. A color monitor is essential because many CADD drawing techniques are based on colors. Monitors are available in various sizes ranging from 13" to 30" or more. Today, average monitors have the ability to display millions of colors.

The main factor that determines the quality of a monitor is the resolution. The term resolution refers to sharpness of an image displayed on the screen. Resolution is measured by the number of picture elements (pixels) that a screen can display. The more pixels and the closer they are, the sharper the image. The distance between pixels is called the "dot-pitch". The smaller the dot-pitch, the sharper the image. A .26 or smaller dot-pitch monitor is recommended for CADD applications.

Printers and Plotters

CADD drawings are printed using fine-quality printers and plotters. Drawings are neat and clean and as accurate as the naked eye can see. You can print drawings at as much as 1200-dpi (dots per inch) accuracy. This means 1200 dots are printed in a one-inch-long line. All the text, dimensions, and other graphics are printed highly accurate, neat and crisp. You can print drawings with a lot of variations; for example, drawings can be printed with different sizes, line types, text fonts and colors.

There are a variety of printers and plotters available in the computer industry. They work on different principles and their prices vary significantly. There are many types of pen plotters, ink-jet printers, laser printers and electrostatic printers. Fig. 1.2 shows an example of an ink-jet plotter.

Ink-jet printers and plotters are the most common. You can buy a small size printer for as little as $200 that can print using 8 1/2"x11" size paper. These printers normally print at 300-600 DPI accuracy, which is quite adequate for CADD drawings. For larger size plots, ink-jet plotters are most common. They can use 36" wide paper. The price range for these plotters is around $5000. For more information on printers and plotters, refer to Chapter 8 *"Printing and Plotting."*

Digitizer, Puck and Mouse

A mouse is the most common pointing device used with CAD. The mouse allows you to control the position of the cursor on the screen by rolling it across a flat surface. Two or three button mice are very common. The left button of the mouse is typically used to select functions from the screen and to enter point locations. The other buttons are configured differently in different CADD programs to display specific menus.

Fig. 1.2: *An example of an ink-jet plotter used for printing CADD drawings.*

Fig. 1.3: *An example of a digitizer used with CADD.*

The digitizer and the puck are additional data input devices that can be used with CADD. A digitizer allows you to enter point locations on the screen and to make selections from the menus. As the puck is moved over the surface of the digitizer, it moves the indicator (cursor) on the screen relatively. To enter a point, you need to position the cursor at the appropriate position on the screen and then press the Enter button on the puck.

Digitizers are available in many sizes and styles. Fig. 1.3 shows an example of a digitizer used with CADD. A number of commands are printed on the digitizer surface. To enter a command, place the puck over the desired command and press the Enter button. The selected command is instantly entered. The puck buttons are configured to perform many other tasks. For example, one button is used to make selections, another to enter the data, another to return to the previous menu and another to cancel the last command.

Some programs support working with a mouse only, while others support both the mouse and the digitizer. The use of digitizer has become uncommon in modern CADD programs.

CADD in a Network Environment

A number of CADD workstations can be connected together by using a computer network. A computer network provides the ability to share both equipment and information. A CADD network is not only cost effective but it provides a great convenience in sharing information.

All the drawings and data can be stored in a common storage medium, which is accessible to all users. You can open any drawing from any workstation in the network and share it with others. This is impossible if computers are not connected in a network.

There are a number of protocols available to connect the computers using a network. Small networks can be created by using network cards and the computers can be connected using a network cable. Bigger networks usually require the use of a server. A server is a dedicated computer that runs a networking program and manages the flow of data between all the computers and devices in a network

Important Note:

When working in a network environment, standard guidelines for file management must be followed. The guidelines may include how to name drawings, how to organize them in directories, how often to save a back-up of the drawings and how to keep a record of changes made to the drawings. These standards enable all the users in the network to work as a team and increase productivity.

CADD Software

A CADD program contains hundreds of functions that enable you to accomplish specific drawing tasks. A task may involve drawing an object, editing an existing drawing, displaying a view of the drawing, printing or saving it, or controlling any other operation of the computer. The functions contain a number of commands that enable you to specify exactly what you want to do and how you want to do it.

The functions are organized into modules that provide easy access to all the commands. Fig.1.5 illustrates a schematic diagram of typical CADD functions in a program. As shown, the program is divided into modules such as draw, edit, data output, function control, data storage and management. A program may also have a number of specialized functions such as layers, database and 3D. Let's have a look at the CADD modules:

- Draw
- Edit
- Data output
- System control
- Data storage and management
- Special features

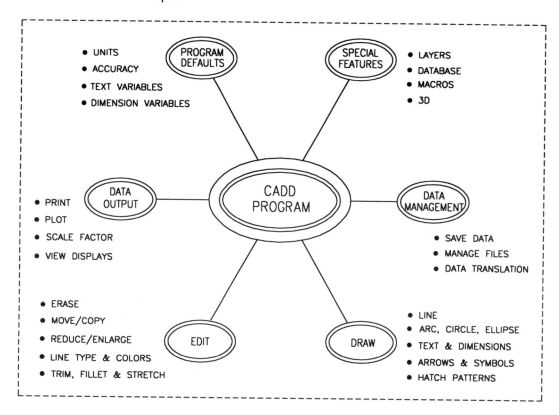

Fig 1.5: *The functions of CADD organized into modules.*

Draw

The draw module provides access to all the drawing functions of CADD. Whenever you need to draw something this group of functions is used. The draw module enables you to draw lines, arcs, circles, ellipses, text, dimensions, symbols, borders and many other drawing components.

Draw is CADD's most frequently used module because all drawing work is accomplished using it.

Edit

The edit module lets you change existing drawing elements and manipulate them in a number of ways. You can move, copy or erase drawing components. You can enlarge or reduce the sizes of diagrams or change the color and line type of drawing components. You can also change the size and style of text and dimensions, as well as edit a dimension to show different units of measurement. A good CADD program is designed to change the appearance of all drawing elements created with CADD.

The edit functions also act as convenient drawing-aid tools. They enable you to join missing corners of lines, trim drawing components along a line, stretch them to fit a new shape, etc. The list of editing capabilities goes on and on. The edit functions make CADD a dynamic drawing tool.

Data Output

The data output module enables you to display drawings on the screen and then print them on paper. There are two separate sets of functions that help accomplish this:

- View-display functions
- Print/plot functions

The view-display functions allow you to display different views of a drawing on the screen. These functions are used quite often, because every time you need to draw something or edit something, you need to focus on that portion of the drawing. With the help of view-display functions, you can zoom in on a specific portion of the drawing.

The print and plot functions allow you to print drawings using a printer or a plotter. You can control many aspects of printing and plotting. You can print the same drawing in different sizes by applying the appropriate scale factor. You can plot the drawings with specific colors, pen thickness, and line types.

Data Storage and Management

The data storage and management module allows you to store and manage drawing data. Through the use of the functions in this module, you can store drawings as files on the hard disk. You can manage the files in directories and sub-directories, and move, copy or delete them as needed.

CADD data management functions also let you translate drawings created by other CADD programs. These functions convert drawing data to a generic format that can be read by any CADD program. Data exchange format (DXF) is one of the common data translation formats used by CADD programs. There are a number of data exchange formats available.

System Control

The system control module (also known as system defaults) allows you to control how CADD works. CADD programs are designed for a broad range of professionals, including architects, designers, engineers and surveyors. With the help of system control functions, you can set the working environment of CADD to suit your needs.

Example: You can set the type of units that you will be using, the accuracy of the units, a style for dimensions and text, colors, layers, line type in a drawing, etc. Additionally, you can customize screen menus, the display of colors on the screen, resolution of the screen, size, the speed of the cursor, etc.

You can also specify whether the selected defaults should apply to a single drawing, to a specific project, or to all the projects in a specific category. The defaults can be set on a temporary or permanent basis.

Special Features

CADD programs usually offer a number of special features that make working with CADD easier and allow you to automate many drawing tasks. For example, you can create layers in a drawing that allow you to segregate drawing components. You can develop spreadsheets and databases that can be used to create many types of project reports. You can create three-dimensional (3D) drawings, such as isometrics and perspectives, with the help of 3D functions. You can also accomplish many other automated tasks with the help of macros.

The number of special features a CADD program has or how elaborate they are varies from one program to another. Some vendors sell specialized features as separate packages, while others include them in a single package. It all depends how a program is written, how big or small it is, and how it is sold.

...rtant Tip:

...nctions of CADD are like the tools of a handyman. All of the tools are ...al for working. Some are used more frequently than others are, but each ...own importance.

...nterface

...ser interface provides the environment and the tools that allow you and ...mputer to communicate. Each CADD program establishes an ...ment that best suits its purpose. The goal is to make working with CADD .... Most programs use a Graphic User Interface (GUI) to communicate ...user. The GUI provides visual aids for quick data entry. You are given ...select functions, enter textual or mathematical data, locate points in the ...window, select objects in the drawing window, etc.

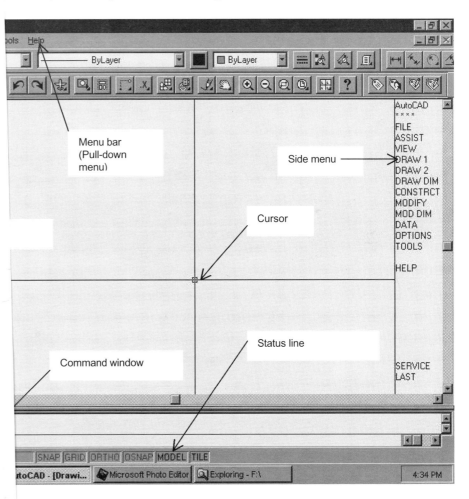

...erface used in AutoCAD.

A typical CADD application window is composed of the following elements: (See Fig. 1.6, an example from AutoCAD)

Command window: An area on the screen that shows all the commands being entered. It also shows what options are available and prompts the user to take action.

Drawing window: The large area in the middle of the application window. All the drawing work is confined within this area.

Menu bar: A horizontal menu located on top that contains the major functions of CADD. When a function is selected from the menu, the menu drops down and displays further options under the menu.

Side menu: A vertical menu that contains all the major functions of the program. To select a function, you need to navigate through the hierarchy of menus and narrow down a selection. The use of side menu has become uncommon in modern CADD programs.

Status line: Shows settings associated with the current drawing on the screen. It shows the current coordinate position of the cursor, current pen number, layer number, etc.

Tool button: A symbol on the screen representing a specific command. When you click on the symbol with the help of the mouse, that particular command is entered.

Tool bar: A collection of tool buttons grouped together. Most CADD programs provide the options to customize the tool bars as required.

The following are the most common ways to communicate with CADD:

- Using the Menu Bar
- Entering commands in the command window
- Using the tool buttons
- Using the dialog boxes
- Working in the drawing area

Using the Menu Bar

Using the menu bar is an important method of selecting CADD functions. Most CADD programs include this user interface and provide quite similar options. Under the File option, drawing saving and data translation utilities are included. The Edit option allows to cut and paste portions of the drawing and import and export data between various applications. A number of other options in the menu bar allow set program defaults and create a customized working environment.

Using the Tool Bars

The tool bars are the latest advancement in the CADD industry. Modern CADD programs use tool bars to provide quick access to commands. The use of tool bars has gained so much popularity that some CADD programs now support only this interface. They don't support command entry through menus, command window or the digitizer.

Using tool bars is a very convenient method of entering commands, because you don't need to type on the keyboard or navigate through the menus. Each command is represented with a specific tool button in the tool bar. To enter a command, all you need to do is click on the tool button with the help of pointing device.

The icons on the tool button suggest the action that the button performs. The exact icons used vary from one program to another, however there are general similarities. Fig.1.7 shows some examples of icons used in CADD. Diagram A shows a drawing tool bar that contains the tool buttons to draw lines, arcs, circle, ellipse, etc. Diagram B shows an editing tool bar that contains the tool buttons for erasing, moving, copying and rotating the drawing elements. Similarly, there are tool bars to display views, printing, plotting drawings and all other CADD functions.

Note:

Most programs allow you to customize the tool bars as needed. You can place frequently used tool buttons in a tool bar, display only specific tool bars, and arrange them on the screen as you like.

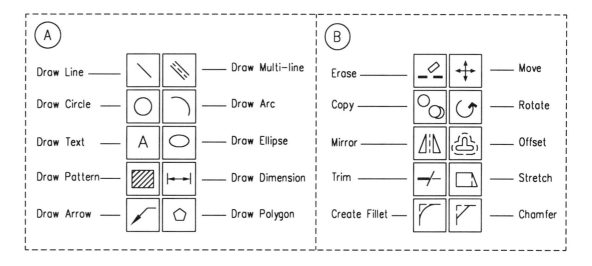

Fig 1.7: *Examples of drawing tool buttons (A) and editing tool buttons (B).*

Entering Commands in the Command Window

The command window is the direct method of entering commands, because you don't need to search through menus. You can enter a command just by typing the command name by using the keyboard. For example, if you want to enter the Line command, simply type the word LINE in the command window and press the Return key and the command is entered.

In many programs, only the initial letter of the command is sufficient to enter the commands. So in our example, only the letter "L" would be required. Most CADD programs allow you to assign any letter or number to a command. You can enter all your favorite commands using these command aliases.

Note:

A drawback of the keyboard entry method is that you need to remember a lot of command names and then type them. An average CADD program has more than 200 commands; it is not always convenient to enter all the commands using the keyboard. Some CADD programs have even eliminated this mode of data entry method.

Working in the Drawing Window

The drawing window is the area where you create a drawing. The drawing window may look small, but it has infinite size like the sky. You can draw as big or as small on this sky like drawing window. The view-display functions allow you to specific views of the drawing.

When you enter a drawing or editing function, the computer displays the prompt as to where you want that action to take place. You often need to enter points in the drawing window to specify when a drawing element is to be drawn or edited. To locate a point all you need to do is place the cursor at a position where you want to enter the point and then press the Enter button on the puck or mouse.

Important tips:

- It is important to take advantage of all the modes of data entry in CADD and discover which methods work best for you. Most CADD programs offer the same functions available through different interfaces. Some functions you may prefer to access through the command window, others using the menu bar or tool buttons.

- The application window designs are constantly being modified. There are endless possibilities as to how commands can be entered, and how the menus and tool buttons can be used. With some knowledge of programming, you can create your own commands, menus and tool buttons.

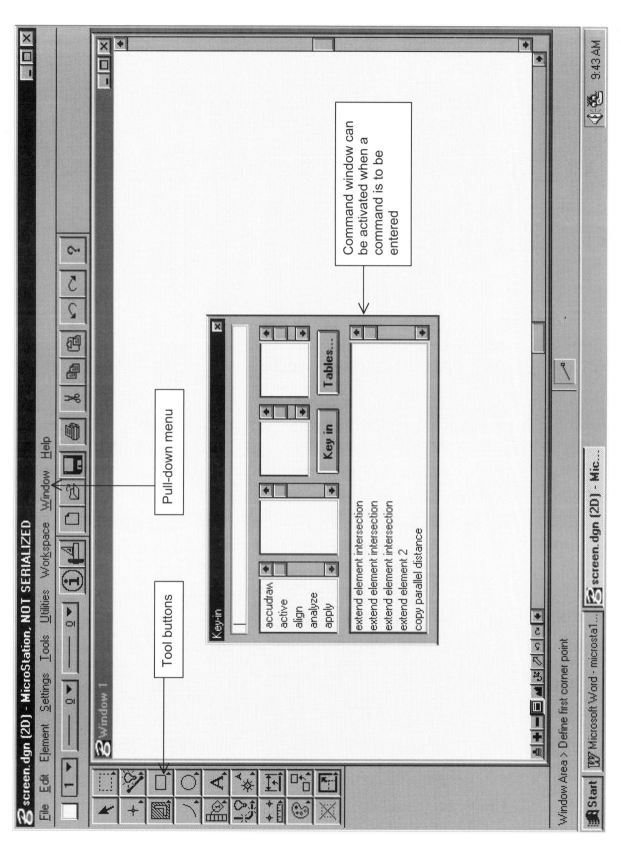

An example of a graphical user interface used in MicroStation.

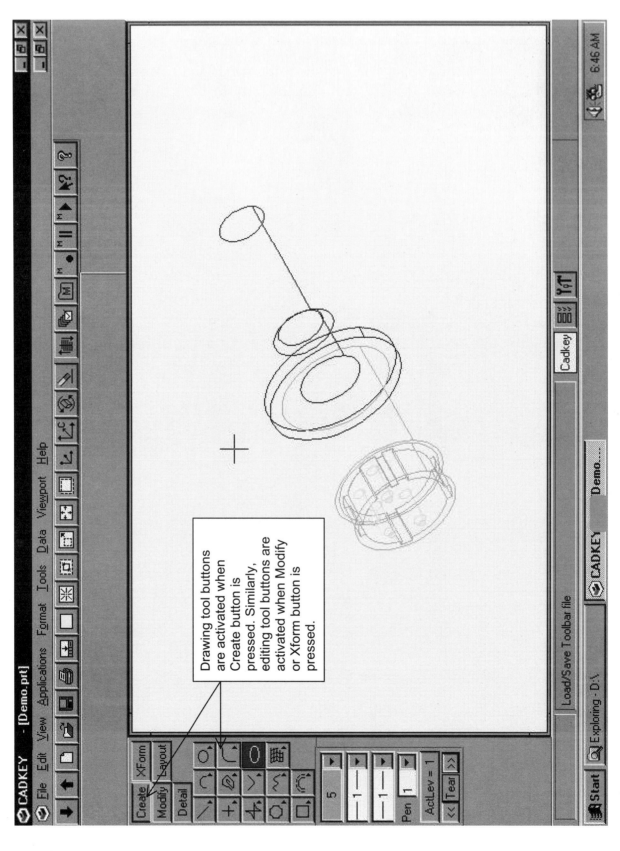

An example of a graphical user interface used in CADKEY.

The CADD Basics

2

Contents

An example drawing created using CADD.

The CADD Basics

About This Chapter

This chapter provides an overview of CADD functions. It describes what various functions will accomplish, how they are organized into CADD menus and how to use them.

You will learn to use basic functions to draw lines or circles, enter text, etc. A brief exercise walks you through the use of these functions. You will also learn how to measure distances and how to locate exact points. This chapter illustrates how to use coordinate methods, such as absolute coordinates, relative coordinates and polar coordinates to measure distances.

In addition, this chapter highlights important principles in setting up CADD drafting standards. It demonstrates how to set up a prototype CADD drawing for a quick start.

Finally, this chapter shows you how to save drawings and where to store them. In this section, you will learn about data saving functions and safety measures to prevent data loss.

Key Terms in this Chapter

Term	Description
Absolute coordinates	Distance measured from a fixed reference point.
Aperture	Effective diameter of the cursor on the screen.
Cartesian coordinates	A rectangular system of measurement to locate points in the drawing area.
Construction line	A line used as a guide to create a framework for the drawing elements.
Isometric	A view of an object tilted at 30° angle on both sides.
Multi-line	A unified drawing element made up of a number of parallel lines that can be drawn just by indicating a starting point and end point.
Object snaps	A method for indicating point locations using existing drawing objects as a reference.
Origin point	The 0,0 location of the coordinate system.
Pattern	A graphical design that can be filled in a specified drawing area.
Polar coordinates	A system to locate the points using an angle and distance.
Polyline	A unified drawing element containing many drawing elements such as lines and arcs.
Prototype drawing	A template drawing that has a number of preset defaults.
Relative coordinates	Distances measured from the last point entered.
Spline	A continuous curved line.
User-defined coordinate system	A mode of measurement that allows the user to set up a customized coordinate system.

Components of a CADD Drawing

CADD drawings are created by drawing individual components (also called drawing objects or entities) of the drawing such as lines, arcs, dimensions and symbols. On a drawing board, you may not notice how many lines and arcs you need to complete a diagram, but with CADD you need to be specific. You need to specify exactly what you want to draw and how you want to draw it. Consider this scenario: drawing a square with rounded edges. Using a drawing board, you would quickly draw four lines and round off the edges with a template. Using CADD to draw the similar square, you will have to draw four lines and four arcs separately. You must specify where each line and arc starts, where it ends, the center point of the arc, the radius, etc.

Fig. 2.1 illustrates the basic drawing components of CADD. As shown, there are lines, arcs, circles, ellipses, symbols, text, dimensions pointers, polylines, borders and patterns. You can complete most of the drawings by using these components of CADD.

To draw any component of the drawing, you need to access a particular drawing command. There are separate commands to draw text, dimensions, patterns, symbols, and other elements of a drawing. The command can be entered by typing it in the command line, selecting it from the menu or by clicking on a specific tool button.

When you enter a command, the screen displays the prompts that guide you through the steps to take to complete a task. For example, when you enter the line command, the screen displays the prompt to enter the starting point and the end point of line. When you enter the arc command, the screen displays the prompt to enter the radius, center point, starting point and end point. Similarly, you need to follow the prompts to draw text, dimensions and symbols.

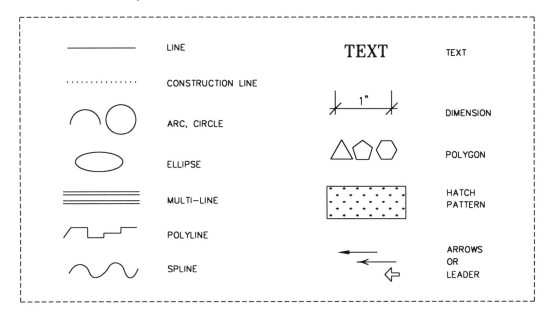

Fig. 2.1: *The components of a CADD drawing.*

Beginning to Draw

Here is a basic exercise using CADD. It is not taken from a specific CADD program. The objective of this exercise is to present an overall picture of how CADD works. It illustrates the concept of using different drawing functions. You don't need to sit in front of a computer to complete this exercise. Just read through the exercise to get a sense of procedures used in CAD.

In this exercise, a drawing tool bar is located on the left side of the screen. For illustration purposes, only the tool buttons used in this exercise are shown. A command window is located at the bottom of the screen that is used to enter commands as well as data. It also displays computer prompts when a specific function is entered using a tool button. The cursor is displayed like a pen that can be moved (with a pointing device) to make selections on the screen.

You will learn how to create a simple diagram using some lines, an arc, text and a dimension. A total of 20 screens (Fig.2.2 to Fig.2.6) illustrate the steps to complete the diagram.

To complete the exercise, the first task is to draw a grid (Fig. 2.2, Screen 1 & 2). The grid points will be used as a guide to draw the rest of the drawing elements. Let's begin…

Step	Action
1	Enter the grid command by typing it in the command window.
2	Screen 2 shows the prompt to enter the grid spacing. Type 6" on the keyboard and then press the Return key. Grid is drawn to fill up the entire drawing window. *Note:* The number of grids displayed depends on the magnification level of the view, which can be adjusted to display appropriate number of grids.
3	Click on the line tool button and the line command is entered.
4	Screen 4 shows the prompt to enter the starting point of the line. Place the cursor on grid number 1 and press the Enter button on the pointing device. *Note:* To enter the point exactly, separate CADD functions called object snaps are used. These functions are discussed later in the chapter.

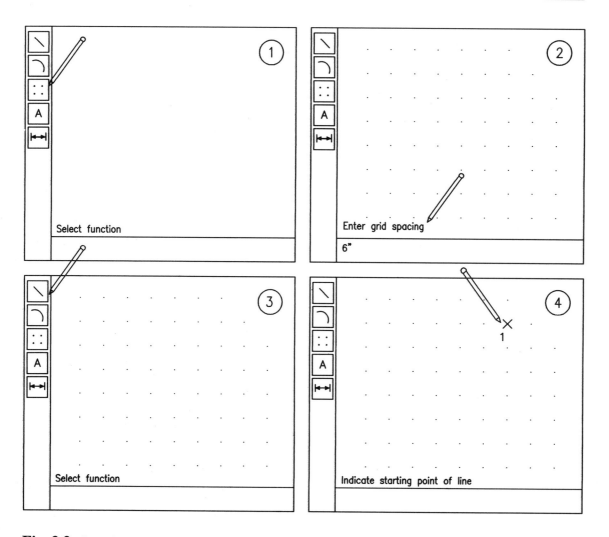

Fig. 2.2: *Drawing a grid.*

The following are the basic steps to draw lines and an arc (Fig. 2.3):

Step	Action
5	Screen 5 shows the prompt to enter the end point of line. Enter a point at the grid point 2 in the same manner as point 1 was entered. A line is drawn from 1 to 2.
6	Screen 6 shows the prompt to enter the end point of the next line. The previous point of line entered automatically becomes the starting point of next line. Continue to draw lines in the same manner from points 3 to 7 as shown. Note: The numbers shown in the illustration are for reference only.
7	Enter the arc command by clicking on the arc tool button.
8	Screen 11 shows the sub-menu with a number of methods for drawing arcs. Select the Center point & radius method. Note: Different methods of drawing arcs are discussed in Chapter 3 "The Drawing Tools."

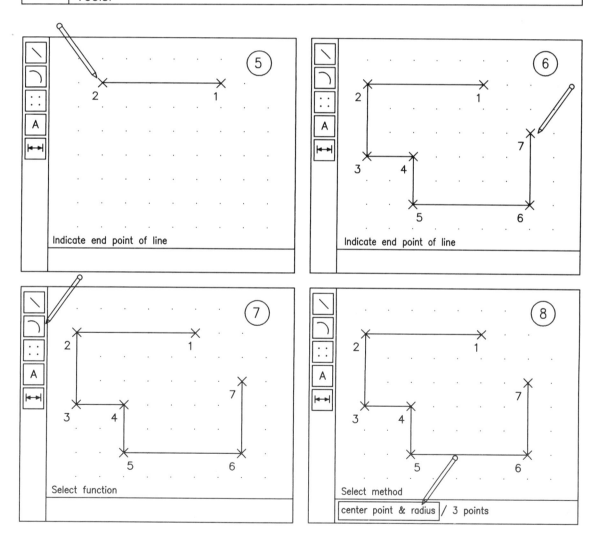

Fig. 2.3: *Drawing lines.*

... continuing to draw an arc (Fig. 2.4):

Step	Action
9	Screen 9 shows the prompt to enter the radius value of the arc. Enter 12" on the keyboard followed by the Return key.
10	Screen 10 shows the prompt to enter the center point of the arc. Enter the center point of the arc at grid point 8.
11	Screen 11 shows the prompt to enter the starting point of the arc. Enter the starting point of the arc at 7.
12	Screen 12 shows the prompt to enter the end point of the arc. Enter the end point of the arc at point 1. An arc is drawn as shown.

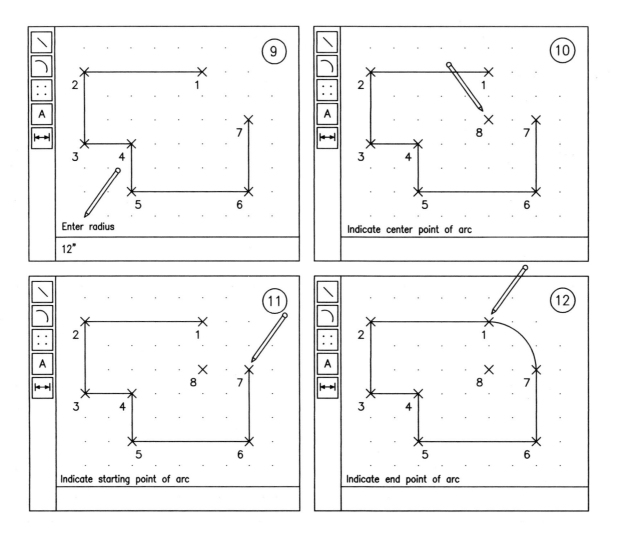

Fig. 2.4: *Drawing an arc.*

The following are the basic steps to write text (Fig. 2.5):

Step	Action
13	Click on the text tool button and the text drawing command is entered.
14	Screen 14 displays different methods of drawing text. Select the standard text option. Note: Different methods of drawing text are discussed in Chapter 3 "The drawing tools."
15	Screen 15 shows the prompt to enter text. Type the word PLAN and then press the Return key.
16	Screen 16 shows the prompt to enter the location of the text. Place the cursor approximately at the bottom of the diagram and press the Enter button on the mouse. The text is drawn as shown. Note: When writing text, it is generally not critical to place text at an exact location. You can locate it by approximation. However, if required, it can be placed at an exact position.

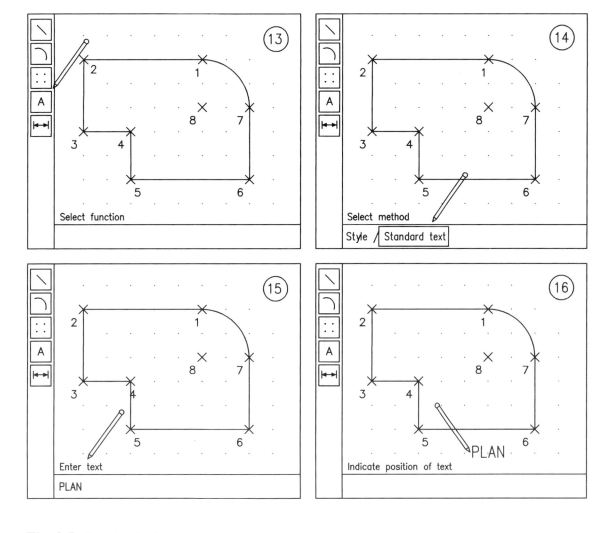

Fig. 2.5: *Drawing text.*

The following are the basic steps to draw dimension (Fig. 2.6):

Step	Action
17	Click on the dimension tool button and the dimension command is entered.
18	Screen 18 shows the sub-menu displaying methods for drawing dimensions. Select the Horizontal option from the sub-menu to draw a horizontal dimension.
19	Screen 19 shows the prompt to enter the first point of the dimension. Place the cursor on grid point 1 and press the Enter button on the cursor.
20	Screen 20 shows the prompt to enter the second point of the dimension. Place the cursor on grid point 2 and press the Enter button on the cursor. A horizontal dimension is drawn as shown. The computer automatically calculated the dimension value and drew appropriate annotations required for the dimension.

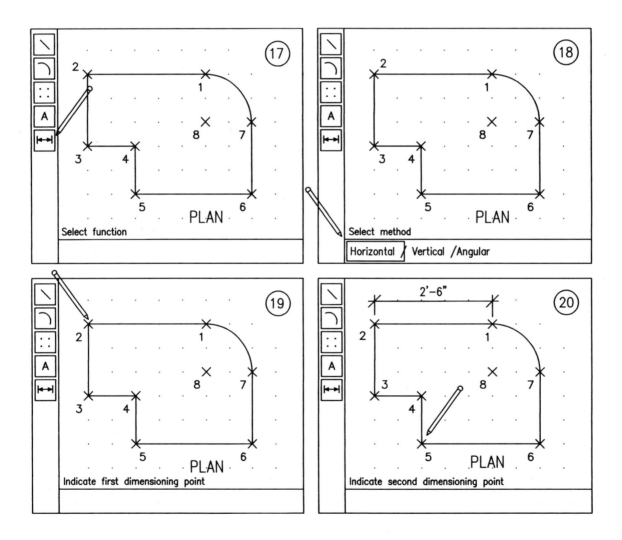

Fig. 2.6: *Drawing dimension.*

Notes:

- In the exercise above, we created nine components of a CADD drawing: six lines, one arc, one text and one dimension. All of these components maintain their own identity. For example, a dimension may be made up of lines and text, but the computer recognizes it as an independent entity. You can move it or edit it in a drawing only as a unified entity.

- CADD keeps track of all the components in a drawing and all the relative data entered to create them. Suppose you draw a 9-inch-long line and later decide to add a 6-inch line to it. Although it will look like one single line on-screen as well on paper, the computer will recognize them as two separate lines.

Locating Points Accurately

In the previous exercise you entered a number of points to draw different drawing elements. The points were entered using the grid points as a reference. However, you can not be certain that the points were entered exactly on the specified grid points. Even if the points were off by $1/100^{th}$ of an inch, this inaccuracy is not acceptable in a CADD drawing.

CADD includes separate functions that enable you to locate points with pinpoint accuracy. These are called object snaps that are included in a point-selection menu or toolbar. You can use a specific object snap tool button to locate a point at a specific point.

Fig. 2.7 shows an example of a point selection toolbar that shows a number of options to locate points. When you want to locate a point exactly at the end point of a line or arc, click on the end point tool button and then indicate a corresponding point in the drawing. The cursor just needs to be near the end point and it automatically snaps to it.

When you need to locate a point at the intersection of lines or arcs, you can use the intersection object snap. To locate a point exactly in the middle of a line, you can use the mid point object snap. Other options in the tool bar allow you to locate points perpendicular to a line, at the center point of a circle, snap to an existing point, etc.

Notes:

- Using object snaps is the key to creating professional CADD drawings. At times, you may feel that you quickly need to finish a drawing and you may save some time without using the object snaps. This will certainly result in an inaccurate drawing. When you dimension this drawing, it will create inaccurate dimensions.

• Most CADD programs allow you to set specific object snaps as a default. When a default is set, you don't need to click on the object snap tool button. The default is automatically used when you enter a point. For example, in the previous exercise, you can set existing point (or grid point) as a default and all the points will be entered exactly on the grid points.

• At times you will find that you are not able to locate a point when you have selected an object snap. It may be that you have selected an object snap, but did not point to the same condition in the drawing. If the computer cannot find the corresponding point, it displays an error message.

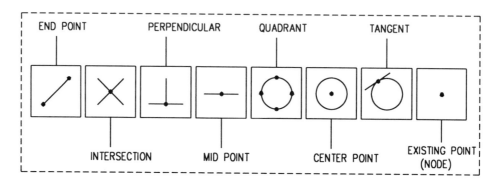

Fig. 2.7: *Object snaps are used to precisely locate points in the drawing area.*

The Coordinate System

The coordinate system is another method of locating points in the drawing area. It enables you to locate points by specifying distances from a fixed reference point. You can locate a point by giving its distance in the horizontal direction, vertical direction, measuring along an angle, etc.

The coordinate system is available when a function requires data input in the form of point locations. You may use it while drawing, editing or any time you need to locate a point. The most common coordinate systems are as follows:

• Cartesian coordinates
• Polar coordinates

Note:

The method of entering coordinates varies from one program to another. For example, in AutoCAD, the coordinates can be entered directly in the command window with the keyboard. In MicroStation and Cadkey, special dialog boxes let you enter the coordinates.

Cartesian Coordinates

Cartesian coordinates is a rectangular system of measurement that enables you to locate points with the help of horizontal and vertical coordinates. The horizontal values, called X-coordinates, are measured along the X-axis. The vertical values, called Y-coordinates, are measured along the Y-axis. The intersection of the X- and Y-axes is called the origin point, which represents the 0,0 location of the coordinate system (Fig. 2.8).

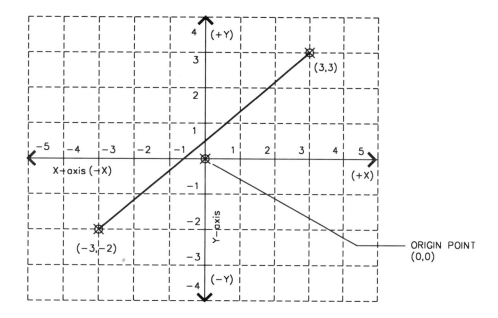

Fig. 2.8: *Measuring distances using Cartesian coordinates.*

The positive X values are measured to the right and the positive Y values are measured above the origin point. The negative X and Y values are measured to the left and below. To enter a coordinate, you need to enter both the X and Y values separated by a comma (X, Y).

Example: To locate a point two units to the right and one unit above the origin point, as shown in Fig. 2.8, enter X = 2, Y = 1 or (2,1). Similarly, to locate a point two units to the left and one unit below, you need to enter X = -2, Y = -1 or (-2, -1). You can use fractions as needed to enter the exact coordinate values.

Polar Coordinates

Polar coordinates allow you to define a point by specifying the distance and the direction from a given point. This mode of measurement is quite helpful in working with angles. To draw a line at an angle, you need to specify how long a line you want to draw and specify the angle.

Fig. 2.9 illustrates the concept of angle measurement commonly used in geometry. You can use any fractions or negative values as required. Diagram B illustrates how you can draw 5" long lines in different directions. To draw the horizontal line, enter the starting point of the line at A. To indicate the end point, enter the angle as 0° and distance 5". Similarly, you can draw a line at 45° and at 90°.

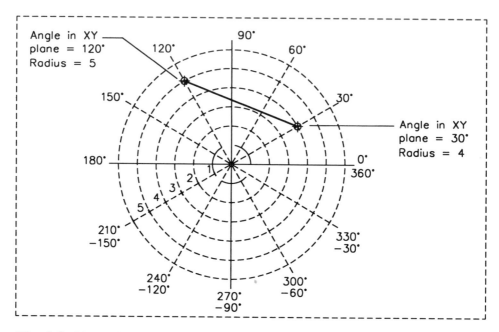

Fig. 2.9: *Measuring distances using polar coordinates.*

The Formats to Enter Coordinates

Cartesian or polar coordinate values can be entered in two formats:

- Absolute
- Relative

Absolute format is a way of measuring distances from a fixed reference location (origin point), which is the 0,0 location of the coordinate system. Consider this point to be stationary at all times. In some CADD programs this point remains visible at the left bottom corner of the drawing area, while in others it is invisible. You can use this point as a reference to measure any distance in the drawing. Absolute coordinates are primarily used to adjust the alignment of diagrams in a drawing, to align one drawing with another or to make plotting adjustments.

Relative format is a way of measuring distances from the last point entered. All measurements are taken the same way as the absolute coordinates, with the only difference being that the relative coordinates are measured from the last point entered instead of the origin point. When a point is entered, it becomes the reference for entering the next point and so on. This mode of measurement is frequently used for drawing because it is always convenient to place the drawing components relative to each other rather than a fixed reference point.

Note:

Each CADD program uses its own annotations to enter absolute or relative coordinates. The task table located at the end of the chapter shows some examples from leading CADD programs.

User-Defined Coordinate System

CADD allows you to create a user-defined coordinate system that can help simplify drawing. When you need to work with a complex drawing that has many odd angles you can create a user-defined coordinate system.

To define a new coordinate system, you need to specify where you want the origin point and the direction of X and Y-axis. Thereafter, the computer works according to this customized coordinate system.

Let's say you need to draw or modify an odd-shaped diagram, such as the one shown in Fig. 2.10. It is very difficult to use cartesian or polar coordinates because they would involve extensive calculations. In this case, you can create a custom coordinate system that aligns with the odd angles of the diagram (28.5° and 118.5°). Now, if you draw a 10 units long line in the X direction by entering cartesian coordinates (X=10, Y=0), it will be automatically drawn at a 28.5° angle.

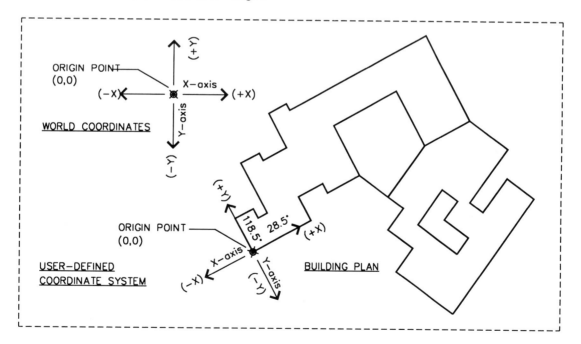

Fig. 2.10: *A user-defined coordinate system can be used to work with odd-shaped diagrams.*

Important tip:

The user-defined coordinate system is especially helpful when you are working with 3D. In a 3D drawing, you need to define each point with three coordinates and work with various surfaces of a 3D model. The user-defined coordinate system allows you to align coordinates with a specific surface, greatly simplifying 3D drawing (illustrated in Chapter 7 "Introduction to 3D").

A Prototype CADD Drawing

A CADD program is designed to meet the needs of a vast number of individuals. It comes with a number of options that can be customized. For example, architects, engineers and surveyors use different annotations to measure units and to draw dimensions. You may have a number of preferences regarding a specific style of text, standard sheet sizes, names of layers, symbol styles, borders, or line types to be used in a project.

When you install a CADD program, it does not have any of the defaults set as per your requirements. You can create a prototype drawing and specify all the defaults that you would like to use. This prototype drawing acts as a template that can be used for all future projects.

When you start a new drawing, you can specify the name of the prototype drawing and all the defaults are taken from this file. This gives you a drawing of a specified size, with border type and all the other defaults set in the prototype drawing. When you start working with CADD, it is better to follow a prototype drawing. It saves a significant amount of time in starting a drawing, because CADD sets everything for you. You are ready to draw instantly.

Most programs allow you to create more than one prototype drawing and save them under different filenames. This is particularly helpful when you are working on several projects that require different drawing standards. Whenever you need to use a specific standard, you can specify the name of that prototype drawing and those defaults are activated.

Note:

CADD programs usually come equipped with a prototype drawing that contains certain preset defaults. These defaults are too general and may not meet your requirements. In most instances, you will need to modify them.

What if You Made a Mistake?

If you make a mistake in issuing a command or in entering any data, you can fix it without many hassles. CADD provides a very convenient way to fix mistakes. Most CADD programs have a built-in function (commonly known as UNDO) that instantly reverses the effect of the last command entered. Many programs allow you to use this function multiple times, so you can go back many steps to fix the mistakes. However, it is always better to take quick action as soon as you realize that a mistake has been made, because the more you go forward with the mistake, the harder it may be to fix it.

When to Save the Drawing or Quit

When you feel that sufficient work has been completed, you should save the drawing. As a guideline, approximately a 15-minute interval is considered appropriate to save your work. This ensures that if you lose your drawing for any reason, you will only lose a maximum of 15 minutes worth of work.

You can save the drawing in two ways: save the drawing with the same name or save the drawing with a different name. When you save the drawing with the same name, it overwrites the old information on the disk with the current information. Before issuing this command, you must ensure that you no longer need the old information. When you save the drawing under a different name, it makes a copy of the drawing and leaves the original data on the disk undisturbed.

There are times when you may not want to save a drawing at all. When you make an irretrievable mistake, you may not want to save it. If you save, it will replace the last updated drawing on the disk with the damaged drawing. If the drawing seems to be damaged, it is better to just exit the drawing. You will lose the work you did since the last time you saved it, but it may be better to revert to the last version of the drawing.

Automatic Data Saving Features

CADD comes with a number of built-in safety features that can help safeguard data. Most CADD programs automatically create a back-up file when you save a drawing. The back-up file contains the original information that was in the file before you saved it. So, if you save a drawing and later realize that you need the earlier version, you can retrieve the original information from the back-up file.

Notes:

- The same back-up file keeps updating when you save the drawing, so you can only retrieve the most recent version. As soon as you realize that you have made a mistake, retrieve the information from the backup file. Do not save the drawing again, because it will overwrite the back-up file.

- You can also set CADD to automatically save your drawing at preset intervals while you're working. This feature keeps on saving the current drawing at regular intervals. If you ever forget to save your drawing and it is lost, you can retrieve it from the automatic save file. The automatic save feature saves the drawing in a separate file without disturbing the original or back-up file.

CADD Filing System

The computer stores information in blocks of data called files. Each drawing created with CADD is stored as a separate data file. Similarly, if you create documents using other programs such as a word processor or spreadsheet, then these too are stored as separate data files.

In addition to data files, system software and application programs have hundreds of files of their own. The computer can be used to store and manage thousands of files depending on the available memory. To manage a large amount of files, good file organization is very important.

Files are organized in directories that make it easy to locate them. A directory is like a file folder that may contain any number of files and sub-directories. Each file is identified by its name, directory and sub-directory.

Fig. 2.11 illustrates the concept of creating directories and sub-directories on a hard disk. As shown, there are separate directories created on the hard disk that contain different programs, drawings and other documents. The drawing directory has three sub-directories under it that contain Architectural, Engineering and Surveying projects. The architectural directory has three sub-directories under it. Finally, there are drawings under project directory PROJECT 1001.

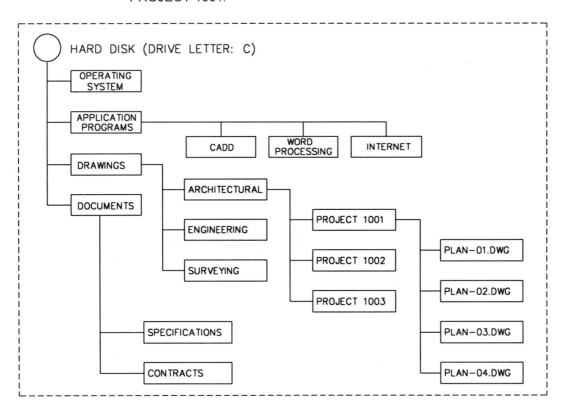

Fig. 2.11: *CADD drawings are stored as individual files and organized into directories.*

There are certain conventions used to name and store drawings. The operating system and the application program you are using establish these parameters. For example, when you are using the Microsoft Windows operating system, a file is located by specifying its name and directory path. To refer to PLAN 01.DWG in the example above, the directory path will look like as follows:

C:/DRAWINGS/ARCHITECTURAL/PROJECT 1001/PLAN-01.DWG

Notes:

- The three letters following the period after the drawing name is called the "file extension". The file extensions are used to specify the kind of information a file contains. The extension .DWG is used to identify drawing files in AutoCAD and in many other programs. MicroStation uses .DGN and Cadkey uses .PRT as drawing file extensions.

- The number of directories and sub-directories that should be created on a disk depends on the number of files that are to be stored. The objective is to group similar information into directories so that the files can be easily located. You may develop any logical system to organize your files. You may decide to organize files according to project titles, dates, geographic location, name of the user, client or project manager.

- US National CADD Standard committee has developed standards to name drawings. Information on these standards can be obtained by logging on to a web site at http://www.nationalcadstandard.org.

A Word about Data Security

The most important task while working on a computer is to safeguard data. Data may be lost due to any number of reasons. Your hard disk may be damaged or data on it may be corrupted. You may forget to save your work and turn off the computer. You may erase a file when you meant only to move or copy it. A computer just follows instructions and takes action in a split second. You can lose hundreds of files within seconds just by pressing a wrong button.

The most important way to safeguard data is to organize your data and take preventive measures. You need to develop standards for naming and organizing files and directories. You need to create directories and sub-directories to store different projects. You need to segregate old work from new work and classify files according to dates, projects, user names, etc.

Make back-up copies of whatever you do. After each working session, store your work on floppy disks as well as the hard disk. Keep a written record of what the files contain. Develop a timetable for how often you will back up your entire hard disk to a back-up tape or other storage device. Keep multiple back-up copies according to dates and time. Store them at a remote location for safekeeping.

Getting Help

One of the first functions you should learn when starting to work with CADD is how to get help. Most CADD programs come with built-in help features that quickly get you started. Getting help is as easy as typing the word Help on the keyboard or selecting it from the menu. Most CADD programs provide help in the following ways:

- You can choose to use a basic tutorial, which is usually provided with the program. This tutorial gives you a quick tour of all the functions in the program.

- You can display an index that lists all the commands available in the program in alphabetical order. You can view topics on any of the commands listed in the index. These topics display the basic capabilities of the command and the steps required completing it.

- You can usually access task-based help in on-line help provided with the program. Most modern programs also provide context-sensitive help, such as help with dialog boxes, which provides the information you need when you need it.

AutoCAD, MicroStation & Cadkey Terms

The following are the important terms used in leading CADD programs:
(The exact procedures vary from one program to another)

Task	AutoCAD	MicroStation	Cadkey
The term for standard mode of measurement	WORLD COORDINATES	GLOBAL COORDINATES	WORLD MODE
The term for user-defined coordinate system	USER COORDINATE SYSTEM (UCS)	AUXILARY COORDINATE SYSTEM (ACS)	DEFINE CONSTRUCTION VIEW
Entering Cartesian coordinates (absolute)	X,Y	X,Y	X,Y
Entering Cartesian coordinates (relative)	@X,Y	DX=X,Y	DXV, DXY,
Entering polar coordinates	Radius<angle in the XY plane	AX=Radius, angle in the XY plane	Enter polar origin, angle and distance
Reversing the effect of the last command issued	UNDO, OOPS	UNDO, OOPS	UNDO, RECALL
File extensions used to identify drawing files	.DWG	.DGN	.PRT
Saving a drawing with the same name	SAVE	SAVE	SAVE
Saving a drawing with a different name	SAVE AS	SAVE AS	SAVE AS
Exit the drawing	QUIT	EXIT	EXIT
Getting help	HELP	HELP	HELP

The Drawing Tools

3

Contents

Contents

The Drawing Tools

About this Chapter

This chapter focuses on the two-dimensional drawing functions of CADD. It describes in detail how to draw each element of a drawing. You will learn the unique characteristics of different drawing elements that make them suitable for specific drawing tasks.

In this chapter you will learn the following:

- *How to create line types such as dotted lines, dashed lines, multi-lines and splines.*

- *How to draw arcs, circles and ellipses.*

- *How to write text and dimensions with different styles and how to control various aspects associated with them such as size, fonts and units.*

- *How to make drawings presentable using drawing annotations such as symbols, arrows, borders and hatching patterns.*

Key Terms in this Chapter

Term	Description
Associative dimensions	A mode of dimensioning that automatically updates dimension values when the dimension size is changed.
Benchmark	A reference point from where all distances are measured.
Spline	A flexible curve that can be drawn to fit any shape.
Hatch patterns	Ready-made patterns that can be added to a specified area in a drawing.
Justification	The alignment of text strings in a specific direction such as to the right, left, or center.
Polyline	A string of lines that may contain a number of line segments connected together.
Tangent	A point on a circle that forms 90° angle between the center point of the circle and another point outside the circle.

The Drawing Tools of CADD

The following are the basic drawing tools found in a CADD program:

- Line types
- Multiple parallel lines
- Flexible curves
- Arcs and circles
- Ellipses and elliptical arcs
- Text
- Dimensions
- Hatch patterns
- Polygons
- Arrows

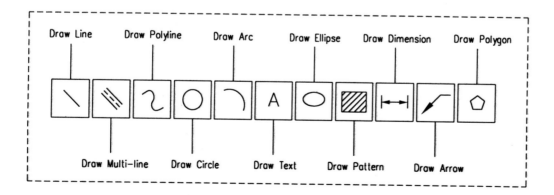

Fig. 3.1: *Some examples of drawing tool buttons used in CADD.*

Using Line Types

There are a number of line types available in CADD that can be used to enhance drawings. There are solid lines (or continuous lines), dash lines, dotted lines, center lines, etc. Fig. 3.2 shows some examples of common line types used in architectural and engineering drawings.

CADD enables you to follow both geometrical and engineering drawing standards. You can use line types to represent different elements in a drawing. For example, in engineering drawings, line types are commonly used to show different building services. In a plumbing plan, one line type can be used to show cold water pipes, one line type for hot water pipes, one line type for waste lines, etc.

CADD is preset to draw solid lines. When you enter the line command and indicate a starting point and end point, a solid line is drawn. If you want to draw with another line type, you need to set that line type as the default. Thereafter, all the lines are drawn with the newly selected line type.

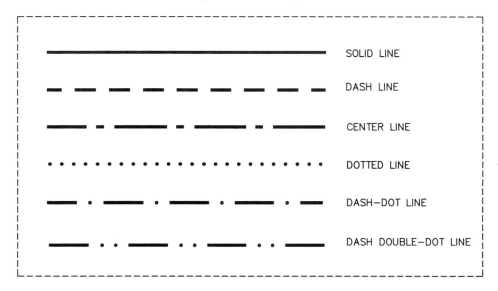

Fig. 3.2: *Common line types used in architectural and engineering drawings.*

Notes:

- International Standards Organization (ISO) has established standard names and definitions for line types. These standards are commonly followed by architects and engineers. US National CAD standard has also established independent standards for line types. For more information visit their web site at http://www.nationalcadstandard.org.

- You can change the line type of an existing line using CADD's edit functions. Some people prefer to first draw everything with one line type and later change line types as needed; others prefer to draw everything with the right line type the first time.

Drawing Multiple Parallel Lines

CADD allows you draw parallel lines (multi-lines) simultaneously just by indicating a starting point and an end point. For example, they can be used to draw the walls of a building plan, roads of a site map, or for any other presentation that requires parallel lines. Fig. 3.3 shows an example of drawing roads using multi-lines.

Most programs allow you to define a style for multiple parallel lines. You can specify how many parallel lines you need, at what distance and if they are to be filled with a pattern or shade.

Specialized CADD programs allow you to add attributes to multi-lines. For example, many architectural CADD software include a special function called "wall'. When you use this function, it automatically draws parallel lines representing walls of specified style and thickness. When you draw a wall, it automatically clears all corners and intersections formed by walls. Advanced CADD programs even allow you to add attributes to the walls such as what kind of wall it is, material, price per linear foot, etc. The computer can keep track of all the walls in a drawing and can prepare a cost estimate using the database. Similar programs allow you to keep track of roadways, pipes, wires, etc. in different engineering disciplines.

Note:

Multiple parallel lines are a unified entity. Even though multiple lines are drawn, they are treated as one line. You cannot erase or edit one line separately. However, there are functions available that can break the entities apart.

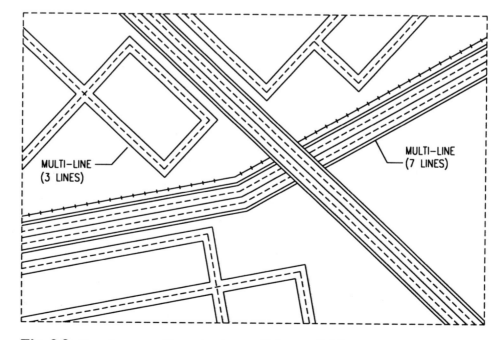

Fig. 3.3: *Drawing a road layout using multiple parallel lines.*

Drawing Flexible Curves

CADD allows you to draw flexible curves (often called splines) that can be used to draw almost any shape. They can be used to create the smooth curves of a sculpture, contours of a landscape plan or roads and boundaries of a map.

To draw a flexible curve, you need to indicate the points through which the curve will pass. A uniform curve is drawn passing through the indicated points. The sharpness of the curves, the roughness of the lines and the thickness can be controlled through the use of related commands.

Diagram A (Fig. 3.4) shows how you can draw a flexible curve by indicating points "1" through "9". You can edit the sharpness of curves and the thickness using the edit functions.

Diagram B (Fig. 3.4) shows how you can draw the contours of a landscape plan using flexible curves. You need to draw seven curves individually to complete the diagram. One of the contours in the diagram shows the actual points used to draw the curve.

Note:

The computer needs a lot of memory to draw flexible curves; they should be used only when necessary.

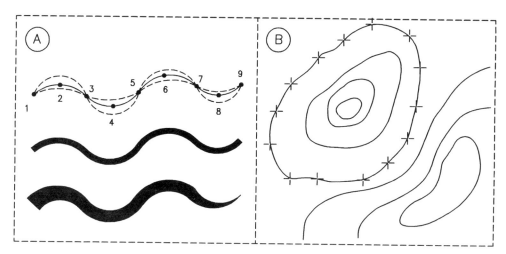

Fig. 3.4: *Drawing flexible curves.*

Important Tip:

There are add-on programs available for surveyors and landscape designers that facilitate drawing contours. These programs also allow you to add intelligent data to the contours such as dimensions from a benchmark and elevations from a datum line. This data can be stored in a database to prepare reports.

Drawing Arcs and Circles

CADD provides many ways to draw arcs and circles. There are a number of advanced techniques available for drawing arcs and circles, which can simplify many geometrical drawing problems. You can draw an arc by specifying circumference and radius, radius and rotation angle, chord length and radius, etc.

Arcs are drawn so accurately that a number of engineering problems can be solved graphically rather than mathematically. Suppose you need to measure the circumference of an arc, just select that arc and the exact value is displayed.

The following are basic methods for drawing arcs and circles:
(These are essentially the same methods you learn in a geometry class. However, when drawing with CADD the approach is a little different.)

- Center point and radius
- 3 points
- Angle and radius
- 2 points
- 2 tangents and a point
- 3 tangents

Center Point and Radius

You can draw an arc or circle by indicating a center point and radius value. The center point can be entered by locating a point in the drawing area. The radius value can be entered numerically using the keyboard or by indicating a point in the drawing area. For example, to enter 1/2" as the radius, you can enter 1/2" using the keyboard or you can indicate a point in the drawing area that is 1/2" away from the selected center point.

To draw an arc, you need to specify two additional parameters: The starting point and the end point of the arc. When you locate these points in the drawing area, an arc is drawn from the starting point to the end point. Diagram A (Fig. 3.5) shows some examples of drawing arcs using this method. The center point of the arc is entered at "1", the starting point at "2" and the end point at "3".

Note:

The arcs are drawn in a counter-clockwise direction from starting point to end point. This is because CADD systems are generally set up to measure the counter-clockwise direction as positive. However, some programs provide the option to set the clockwise direction as the positive direction as well. In doing so, the arcs are drawn the opposite way.

3 Points

You can draw an arc or circle that passes through three given points. You need to enter three points through which the arc or circle will pass. Diagram B (Fig. 3.5) shows some examples of drawing arcs and a circle using this method. The points "1", "2" and "3" are used to draw the arcs and the circle.

Note:

If a circle or arc can't be drawn through the three points you entered, the computer will display an error message to that effect.

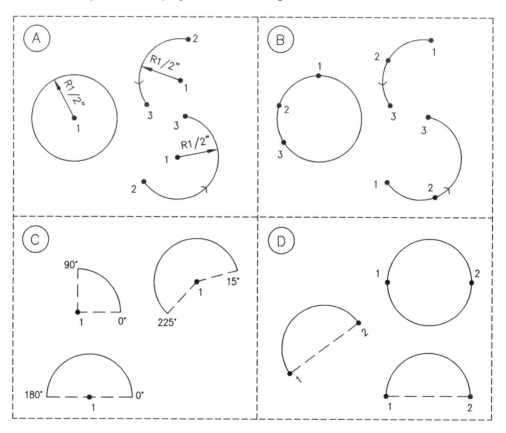

Fig. 3.5: *Drawing arcs and circles.*

Radius and Rotation Angle

You can draw an arc by specifying a radius and rotation angle. The radius value determines the size of the arc and the rotation angle determines where the arc starts and ends. You need to enter a center point, radius, starting angle and ending angle of the arc.

Diagram C (Fig. 3.5) illustrates some examples of drawing arcs using this method. In this diagram, the center point of the arc is entered at "1" and two angles are specified. For example, to draw the semi-circular arc, 0° is entered as the starting angle and 180° as the ending angle.

2 Points

You can draw a circle or semi-circular arc just by indicating two points. The two points you enter determine the diameter of the circle, and an arc or circle is drawn passing through these points. Diagram D (Fig. 3.5) illustrates some examples of drawing arcs and a circle using this method. Just enter point "1" and "2", and the arc or circle is drawn.

2 Tangents and a Point

You can draw a circle tangent to two lines and passing through a given point. You need to indicate the two lines and a point within the lines. Diagram A (Fig. 3.6) illustrates an example drawing a circle using this method.

Note:

The point through which the circle passes must be entered inside the two given lines. If it's entered outside the lines, the computer can't draw a circle and an error message to this effect is displayed.

3 Tangents

You can draw a circle tangent to three given lines. Using this method, all you need to do is indicate the three lines. No radius value is required because there can be only one circle tangent to three lines. A circle drawn using this method is shown in Diagram B (Fig. 3.6).

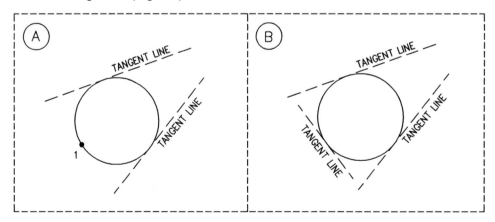

Fig. 3.6: *Drawing arcs and circles.*

Note:

The number of methods available to draw arcs and circles and the exact procedures used vary from one program to another. Advanced engineering programs include a number of additional methods for drawing arcs and circles. For example, you can draw an arc by specifying its circumference and radius or circumference and rotation angle.

Drawing Ellipses and Elliptical Arcs

Ellipses are much easier to draw with CADD than on a drawing board. On a drawing board, you need to find the right size template or draw a series of arcs individually to draw an ellipse. With CADD, all you need to do is specify the size of the ellipse.

The following are two basic methods for drawing ellipses:

- Length and width
- Axis and rotation angle

Length and Width

An ellipse has two axes: a major axis and a minor axis (Fig. 3.7). The major axis determines the length of the ellipse and the minor axis determines the width.

To draw an ellipse you need to specify length and width, i.e., major axis and minor axis. You can enter the values numerically or by indicating points in the drawing area. When you need to draw an ellipse rotated at an angle, you can indicate the axis rotated at an angle (Fig. 3.7). To draw an elliptical arc, enter the starting point and the end point of the ellipse in addition to indicating the axes.

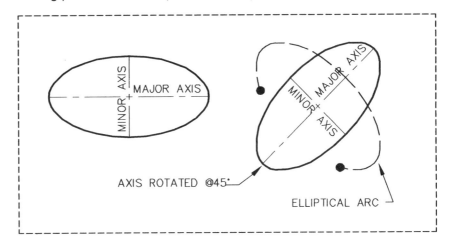

Fig. 3.7: *Drawing ellipses by specifying length and width.*

Axis and Rotation Angle

When a circle is viewed at an angle, it takes on an elliptical shape. CADD uses the same principle to draw an ellipse. It takes a circle and rotates it into 3D space around one of the axes. As a result, the width of the circle is reduced and an ellipse is drawn (Fig. 3.8).

To draw an ellipse, you need to specify the length of the ellipse (major axis) and the rotation angle. The computer automatically calculates its width and draws an ellipse.

Fig. 3.8 illustrates how a circle creates an ellipse when rotated at different angles. In the first diagram, 0° is entered as the rotation angle; this draws a complete circle. As you enter a higher angle value, the ellipse gets smaller and smaller. Most CADD programs don't allow you to enter a rotation angle greater that 89.4°. This is because the ellipse becomes so narrow that it appears as a line and the computer displays an error message.

Note:

In advanced engineering systems, a number of additional methods for drawing elliptical arcs are available. These methods enable you to draw a variety of elliptical shapes, including a parabola and a hyperbola.

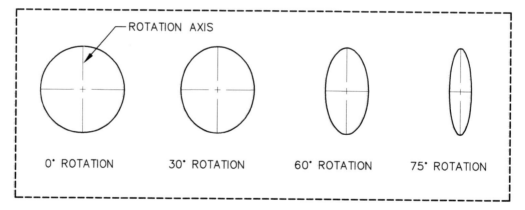

Fig. 3.8: *Drawing ellipses with axis and rotation angle method.*

Adding Text to Drawings

CADD allows you to add fine lettering to your drawings. You can use text to write notes, specifications and to describe the components of a drawing. Text created with CADD is neat, stylish and can be easily edited. Typing skills are helpful if you intend to write a lot of text.

Writing text with CADD is as simple as typing it on the keyboard. You can locate it anywhere on the drawing, write it as big or as small as you like and choose from a number of available fonts.

Note:

When large amounts of text are added to drawings, it slows down the screen displays. Many programs provide options to temporarily turn off text or to display text outlines only. This feature helps save computer memory and speeds up the display of screen images. The text can be turned back on whenever needed.

The following are the basic factors that control the appearance of text:
(The exact terms and procedures used vary from one program to another.)

- Text height
- Height to width ratio and inclination of letters
- Special effects
- Alignment of text (justification)
- Text fonts

Text Height

You can write any size text by specifying the height of letters. It is a good idea to develop a set of standards determining what size text to use where. For example, you can use 1/16" or 3/32" text height for descriptive text, 1/8" height for sub-titles and 1/4" for main titles (Diagram A, Fig. 3.9). The height standard you choose for text in one drawing should be followed on all drawings in a project. This presents a uniform look to each drawing in the project.

Note:

The height of text you use is reduced or enlarged depending on the scale factor applied to drawings when they are plotted. Accordingly, you need to enter smaller or bigger text. We will discuss more on this in Chapter 8, "Printing and Plotting."

Height to Width Ratio and Inclination of Letters

CADD allows you to fine-tune the text in a number of ways. You can specify a height-to-width ratio for all the letters, indicate spacing between the letters and even make the letters inclined.

Diagram B (Fig. 3.9) illustrates how the text appearance is altered with a different height to width ratio. Diagram C (Fig. 3.9) illustrates how you can change the appearance of text by inclining it to a specific angle.

Special Effects

Sometimes you need to write text rotated at an angle, written in a vertical direction, or even mirrored. Many CADD programs provide these special options that can be used for specific drawing conditions. Diagram D (Fig. 3.9) illustrates some examples of drawing rotated, mirrored and vertical text.

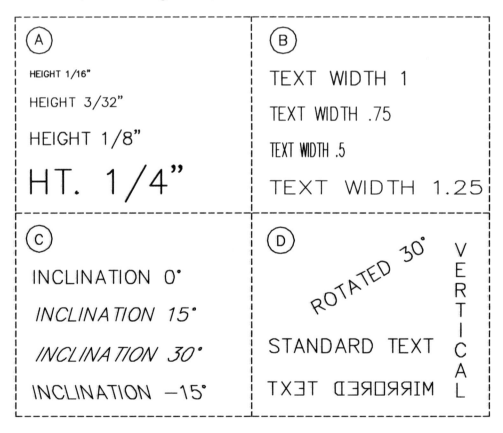

Fig. 3.9: *Drawing text with varying height, ratio, spacing and inclination.*

Alignment of Text (Justification)

The term justification is commonly referred to as the alignment of text. The text can be aligned to the left (left justified), aligned to the right (right justified) or centered (center justified). Fig. 3.10 illustrates examples of text written with left, centered or right justification. You can specify justification for individual lines or paragraphs.

```
This paragraph          This paragraph               This paragraph
shows                        shows                             shows
how you can              how you can                   how you can
write text                 write text                      write text
with                          with                              with
left-justification.   center-justification.     right-justification.
```

Fig. 3.10: *Drawing text with justification.*

Text Fonts

CADD offers many fonts that allow you to write text with different styles. You can choose from dozens of fonts available in CADD. A number of fonts are also available through independent vendors. Fig. 3.11 illustrates some of the common fonts. You can give your drawing whatever presentation you want by selecting an appropriate font.

Arial Rounded Bold	ARCH	ALGERIAN
BANKGOTHIC	CityBlueprint	AWOLF
Bookman Old Style	CountryBlueprint	Braggadocio
Century Gothic	gothice	HELVETICA
Comic Sans MS	scripts	SHADOW
Courier New	Brush Script	Vineta BT
Times New Roman	Commercial Script	Wide Latin

Fig. 3.11: *Drawing text using different fonts.*

Notes:

- Most CADD developers include proprietory fonts with their software. Font names change from one program to another.

- The fonts used in a drawing must be supported by the printer or plotter used for printing the drawing. You may want to do a test plot before using specific fonts in a drawing.

- When sending drawings electronically, make sure to include the fonts used in the drawing. Otherwise, the recipient may not be able to open the drawings.

- You can change the appearance of text using the editing functions of CADD. You can change the height, width, inclination, rotation, spacing, fonts, justification, etc., as needed.

Defining a Text Style

As discussed, there are a number of factors that control the appearance of text. It is time-consuming to specify every parameter each time you need to write text. CADD allows you to define text styles that contain all the text information such as size, justification and font. When you need to write text, simply select a particular style and all the text thereafter is written with that style. CADD offers a number of ready-made text styles as well.

Important Tip:

There are a number of add-on programs available that can make working with text faster and easier. These programs provide basic word-processing capabilities that can be used to write reports and make charts. They provide access to a dictionary and thesaurus database that can be used to check spelling and to search for alternative words.

Drawing Dimensions

CADD's dimensioning functions provide a fast and accurate means for drawing dimensions. To draw a dimension, all you need to do is to indicate the points that need to be dimensioned. CADD automatically calculates the dimension value and draws all the necessary annotations.

Fig. 3.12 illustrates the basic components of a CADD dimension. The annotations that form a dimension are: dimension line, dimension text, dimension terminators and extension lines. You can control the appearance of each of these elements by changing the dimensioning defaults.

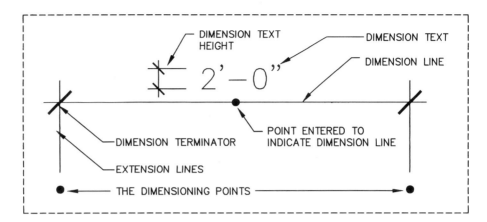

Fig. 3.12: *The components of a dimension.*

The following are the common methods for drawing dimensions:

- Drawing horizontal and vertical dimensions
- Dimensioning from a base line
- Dimensioning arcs and circles
- Drawing dimensions parallel to an object
- Dimensioning angles

Drawing Horizontal and Vertical Dimensions

You can draw horizontal or vertical dimensions between any two points. Even if the points you indicate are not aligned horizontally or vertically, the computer automatically calculates the horizontal or vertical distance between the points and draws the dimension.

Diagrams A and B (Fig. 3.13) illustrate some examples of horizontal and vertical dimensions. The dots shown in the diagram are the dimensioning points that were entered to draw the dimensions.

Most CADD programs allow you to draw a string of dimensions. When you have finished drawing the first dimension, the next dimension can be drawn just by indicating the next dimensioning point. It is always better to start dimensioning from one corner and continue towards another.

Dimensioning from a Baseline

You can draw a series of dimensions measured from a single reference point. This mode of measurement is often referred to as baseline, benchmark or datum. To draw dimensions from a baseline, you need to draw the first dimension by indicating the dimensioning points and the dimension line. The rest of the dimensions are automatically drawn measured from the baseline, that is, the first point you entered. Diagram C (Fig. 3.13) illustrates some examples of benchmark dimensions that are taken from the left corner of the diagram.

Dimensioning Arcs and Circles

To dimension arcs and circles, all you need to do is indicate the arc or circle and a dimension showing the radius or diameter value is drawn. All necessary annotations are automatically drawn. You can choose from a number of annotation styles available.

Drawing Dimensions Parallel to an Object

You can draw dimensions parallel to any two indicated points. It gives the exact distance between the indicated points. This mode of dimensioning is quite helpful for dimensioning odd-shaped diagrams. The dimension line is automatically drawn parallel to the indicated points. Diagram D (Fig. 3.13) shows two examples of drawing dimensions parallel to lines.

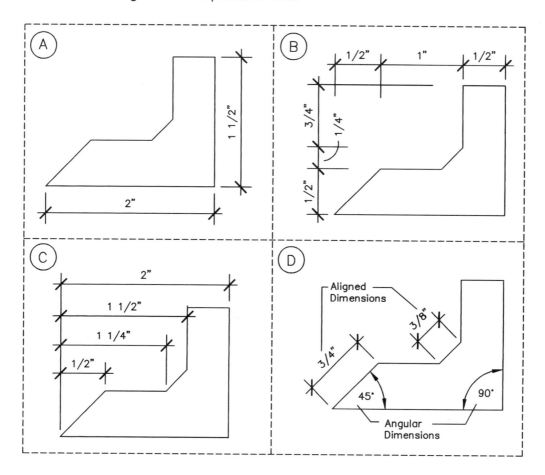

Fig. 3.13: *Drawing dimensions.*

Dimensioning Angles

CADD allows you to dimension an angle formed by two lines. To draw an angular dimension, you just need to indicate the two lines. The computer automatically calculates the angle between them and draws all the necessary annotations required for the dimension. Diagram D (Fig. 3.13) illustrates two examples of drawing angular dimensions.

Important Tip:

The key to drawing accurate dimensions is to have an accurate drawing and to indicate the dimensioning points accurately. When you first draw diagrams, they must be accurate so that when you indicate the dimensioning points, exact dimensions are drawn. If the diagram is inaccurate, it is reflected in the dimension values.

Writing Dimensions with Different Units

CADD enables you to draw dimensions with units commonly used in architecture and engineering drawings. The dimension can be drawn in feet-inches or by the metric system. Diagram A (Fig. 3.14) illustrates how the same dimension can be written with different units of measurement. The top dimension is written with architectural units using feet-inches. The following dimensions are written with engineering units, decimal units and fractional units.

When you start a drawing, you can specify the units that you will be using and the level of accuracy required. All dimensions are drawn according to that mode of measurement and accuracy. The level of accuracy that you should use for a drawing generally depends upon the scale of the drawing. When you are working on large-scale drawings, you may want to set a lesser degree of accuracy to avoid unnecessary fractions. When you are working with minute details, you may want to set a higher degree of accuracy.

Diagram B (Fig. 3.14) illustrates how the same dimension is written at varying levels of accuracy. The top dimension is written with an accuracy of 1/16" using architectural units; the following dimensions use accuracy set to 1/8", 1/4" and 1/2". As shown, the fractions are rounded off to the nearest fraction when the level of accuracy is changed.

Note:

You can change the dimensions from one mode of measurement to another or change their appearance using CADD's edit functions. For example, the dimensions created with feet-inch units can be easily converted into the metric system with a few simple steps. Similarly, you can edit the text size, font, and dimension terminators, etc.

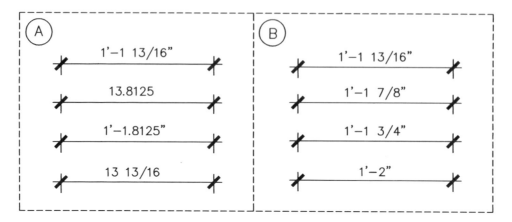

Fig. 3.14: *Drawing dimensions using different units.*

Setting Dimension Styles

CADD provides a number of options for controlling the appearance of dimensions. You can assign styles to dimension text, dimension terminators, etc. Almost all styles that are available to draw text with CADD are available to draw the dimension text as well. Diagram A (Fig 3.15) illustrates examples of dimensions written with different text styles. It is a good idea to use the same size and style for dimension text as for other descriptive text used in a drawing. This gives a uniform look to drawings.

You can choose from a number of dimension terminators. Diagram B (Fig 3.15) illustrates examples of common terminators used in CADD. You can also specify a number of other parameters, such as the size of terminators, thickness of dimension lines, length of the extension lines, distance of text from the extension line and distance of extension lines from dimension points.

CADD allows you to pre-define dimension styles that contain information about dimensions. You can specify all the dimensioning parameters, such as text height, width, ratio, font and terminators in a style. When you need to write a dimension with a specific style, simply select that dimension style from the menu.

Important Tips:

- Most CADD programs allow you to add special annotations that appear with specific dimensions. You can add prefixes or suffixes such as "(+/-)", "field verify", "typical", "hold this dimension" and "not to scale". These annotations are commonly used in engineering drawings for specific drawing conditions.

- When CADD diagrams are reduced or enlarged using editing commands, the dimension values are updated automatically. This enhanced dimensioning feature is called "associative dimensioning". Previously, associative dimensioning was available only in advanced CADD programs, but it is now used in almost all CADD programs.

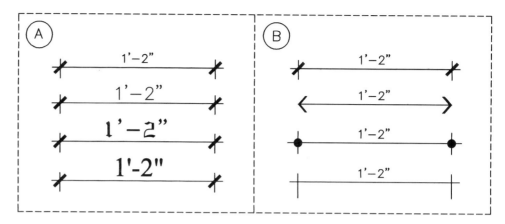

Fig. 3.15: *Drawing dimensions using styles.*

Adding Hatch Patterns to Drawings

The look of CADD drawings can be enhanced with the hatch patterns available in CADD. The patterns can be used to emphasize portions of the drawing and to represent various materials, finishes, and spaces. Several ready-made patterns are available in CADD that can be instantly added to drawings. Fig. 3.16 illustrates some common examples of hatch patterns.

Hatch patterns are quite easy to draw. You don't need to draw each element of a pattern one by one. You just need to specify an area where the pattern is to be drawn by selecting all the drawing objects that surround the area. The selected objects must enclose the area completely, like a closed polygon. When the area is enclosed, a list of available patterns is displayed. Select a pattern, and the specified area is filled.

Fig. 3.16: *A number of ready-made hatching patterns are available in CADD.*

Important Tip:

A number of hatch patterns are available through independent CADD vendors. These pattern libraries are designed to help professionals in all fields. Many CADD programs allow you to create custom patterns as well. You can modify the existing patterns or define new patterns by adjusting the elements of a pattern.

Drawing Symbols

Symbols provide a convenient way to draw geometrical shapes. You may compare this function with the multi-purpose templates commonly used on a drawing board. To draw a geometrical shape, such as a pentagon or hexagon, select an appropriate symbol from the menu, specify the size of the symbol, and it is drawn at the indicated point. Some examples of symbols are shown in Diagram A (Fig.3.17).

Drawing Arrows

Arrows (or pointers) in a drawing are commonly used to indicate which note or specification relates to which portion of the drawing, or to specify a direction for any reason. There are several arrow styles available in CADD programs. Some common examples are shown in Diagram B (Fig. 3.17). You can choose from simple two-point arrows to arrows passing through a number of points, and from simple to fancy arrow styles. To draw an arrow, you need to indicate the points through which the arrow will pass.

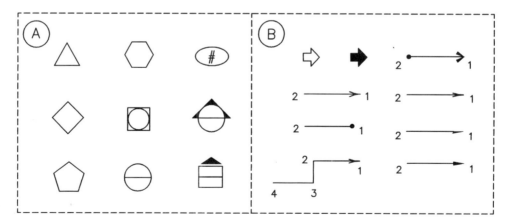

Fig. 3.17: *Drawing symbols and arrows.*

The Artistic Side of CADD

CADD provides only limited capabilities for artistic expression. It contains the basic tools to draw freehand lines, random hatch patterns, etc. To draw a freehand line, you just need to press and hold the mouse button and move the cursor where you want to draw the line. This drawing principle is commonly used in paint programs, which are primarily intended to create artistic designs.

The concept of CADD is quite different from paint programs. CADD programs are object-oriented, meaning you create objects such as lines and arcs that have their own identity. Paint programs are usually pixel-oriented; meaning everything is made up of pixels (picture elements). You can move or edit pixels individually and arrange them in any shape you like.

Most CADD programs allow you to import a scanned image or an image created by a paint program into a CADD drawing. The imported image is recognized as being made up of individual pixels, which can be edited individually.

AutoCAD, MicroStation and Cadkey Terms

The following are the important terms used in leading CADD programs:
(The exact procedures vary from one program to another)

Task	AutoCAD	MicroStation	Cadkey
Multiple parallel lines	MLINE	MULTI-LINES	N/A
Drawing flexible curves	PLINES/SPLINE	PLACE BSPLINE	CREATE SPLINE
Drawing an arc	ARC	PLACE ARC	CREATE ARC
Drawing a circle	CIRCLE	PLACE CIRCLE	CREATE CIRCLE
Drawing an ellipse	ELLIPSE	PLACE ELLIPS	CREATE ELLIPSE
Writing text	DTEXT, MTEXT	PLACE TEXT/ PLACE NOTE	LABEL, NOTE
Drawing dimensions	DIM: HORZ/VERT/	DIMENSION:ANGLE/ ELEMENT/AXIS	DIMENSN:
Drawing hatch patterns	BHATCH	HATCH, PATTERN AREA/ ELEMENT	X-HATCH, PATTERN/CREATE
Drawing polygons	POLYGON	PLACE BLOCK, PLACE SHAPE	CREATE N-GON
Drawing arrows	DIM: LEADER	PLACE TERMINATOR	ARR/WIT, LEADER

Important Tip:

Most CADD programs provide programming tools to customize the working environment. With knowledge of programming, you can modify the functions to work precisely as per your requirements.

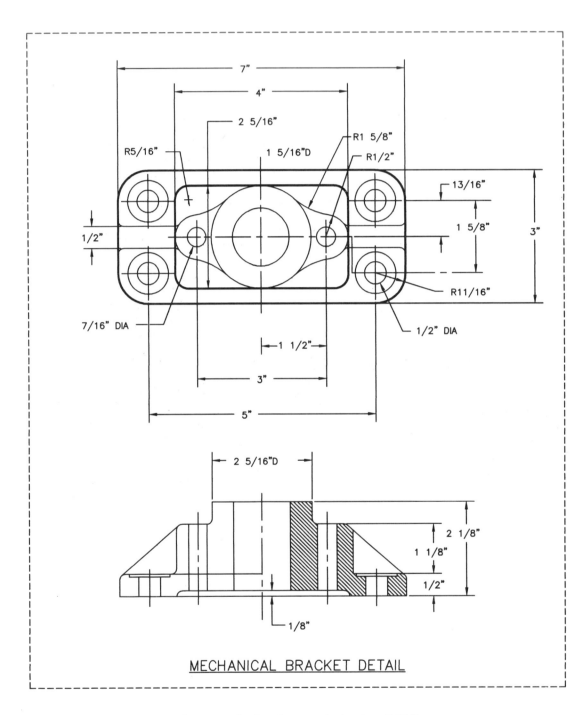

MECHANICAL BRACKET DETAIL

An example drawing created using CADD.

View-Displays

4

Contents

An example of a PC based computer system using CADD software.

View-Displays

About this Chapter

This chapter describes CADD's view-display functions. These functions allow you to display different views of a CADD drawing. They make it possible to work on various portions of a drawing. You can move the image on the screen to display a desired view and enlarge or reduce the images as required.

Key Terms in this Chapter

Term	Description
Pan	To move the view in a specific direction.
Zoom in	To get a closer view.
Zoom out	To get a view from a greater distance.
Zoom factor	To enlarge or reduce the view by a specific degree.
Viewport	A portion of the drawing window that contains an independent view of the drawing.
Window	An imaginary rectangle formed by the indicated points.

The View-Display Functions

CADD's view-display functions enable you to display different views of the drawing. You need to constantly change views in order to work on different portions of the drawing. For example, to draw a line from one corner of a large drawing to another, you may need to change the three views. First, magnify the corner where the line is to be started. Second, reduce the display to see the entire drawing. Third, magnify the corner to indicate the end point of the line.

Working with the view-display functions is similar to using a telescopic camera. You can zoom out to view larger objects, and zoom in to get a closer view of objects. However, CADD's functions are much more precise and flexible. You can magnify the drawings to an exact degree, store specific views in computer memory, and then display them back when required.

The following are the basic techniques to display views:

- Display a full view
- Move the view
- Zoom-in and zoom-out
- Enlarging view by indicating a window
- Saving and displaying views
- Display previous view

You can enter view-display functions in the command window or by using the tool buttons. Fig. 4.1 shows some examples of tool buttons used to enter view display functions. The exact icons used vary from one program to another.

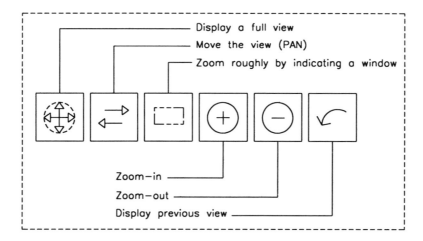

Fig. 4.1: *Examples of view-display tool buttons.*

To illustrate the view-display functions, we will use an engineering drawing shown in Fig. 4.2. The drawing shows mechanical parts of a machine in minute detail. We will illustrate how to work on this complex drawing using view-display functions.

Note:

The use of view display does not change the size of drawing objects in any way. They are just displayed at a specific magnification level.

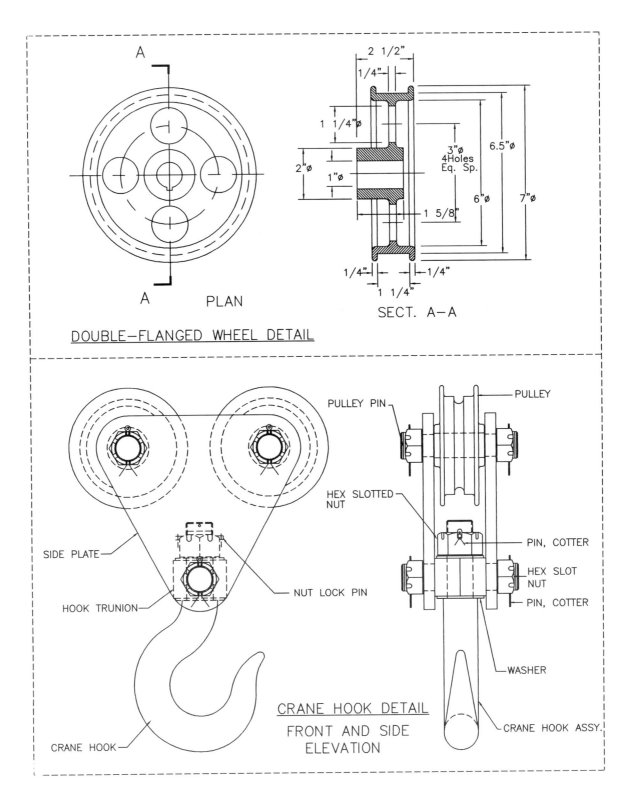

Fig. 4.2: *An engineering drawing showing plan, section and elevation of a mechanical part.*

Displaying a Full View

CADD allows you to display the entire drawing on-screen regardless the size of the drawing. If the drawing is too large, CADD automatically reduces it to fit the drawing area. If the drawing is too small, CADD automatically enlarges it to fill the drawing area.

Example: If you draw a 1"x1" square and display a full view of the drawing, it magnifies the image to fill the entire screen. Now let's say you draw a 10' diameter circle around the square and then display a full view. It will automatically reduce the entire image to fit that circle on the screen. The square will be reduced significantly and might look like only a dot.

Fig. 4.3 (Screen 1) illustrates how you can display the entire drawing (Fig. 4.2) to fit on-screen by clicking on the full view tool button.

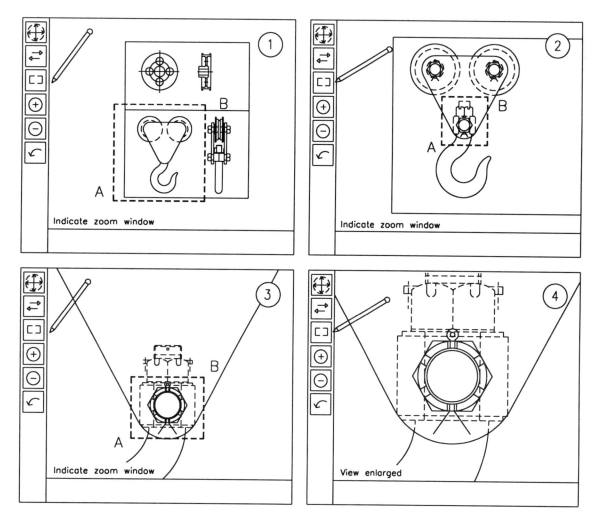

Fig. 4.3: *The drawing image can be enlarged, reduced or moved using view-display functions.*

Moving the View

You can move the image in any direction with the push of a button. This capability of CADD is often referred to as "pan". To move the image, all you need to do is indicate two points between which the drawing should move. The drawing is moved from the first indicated point to the second indicated point. Screen 2 (Fig. 4.3) shows how you can move the drawing to the left by indicating points A and B.

In some CADD systems the same result is achieved by pressing the arrow keys on the keyboard or by using the scroll bars on the screen. The drawing is moved in the direction of the arrow key pressed. You can preset a percentage of how much the drawing should move with each press of an arrow key.

Zoom-in and Zoom-out

CADD allows you to reduce or enlarge the image view by a specified degree. You can enter a specific percentage or a zoom factor to reduce or enlarge an image. To enlarge the image 1 1/2 times, you need to enter the percentage value as 150% or the zoom factor as 1.5. To reduce the image by half, you need to enter the percentage value as 50% or zoom factor as 0.5.

Most of the CADD programs provide tool buttons that allow you to instantly zoom-in and zoom-out by a predefined percentage. For example, clicking on the zoom-in tool button enlarges the image by 150% and clicking on the zoom-out button reduces the image by 50%.

Screen 3 (Fig. 4.3) shows how you can reduce the image shown on Screen 2 by 50%. Simply click on the zoom-out tool button and the image is reduced as shown.

Enlarging View by Indicating a Window

You often need to enlarge drawing images in order to work with a greater detail. You can specify an area to be enlarged by designating an enlargement window on the screen. A window is an imaginary rectangle formed by two diagonal points. The section of diagram contained within the window is enlarged to fit the entire drawing area.

Fig. 4.4 shows how you can enlarge a portion of the diagram by indicating a window. Screen 1 shows the full view of the drawing. Click on the zoom window tool button to enlarge a corner of the drawing and enter points A and B as the corners of the enlargement window. The view is enlarged as shown on Screen 2. To view the drawing in more detail, enter the zoom window command again and enter points A and B as the corners of enlargement window. The view is enlarged as shown on Screen 3. Similarly, enlarge the view again to see the drawing in more detail as shown on Screen 4.

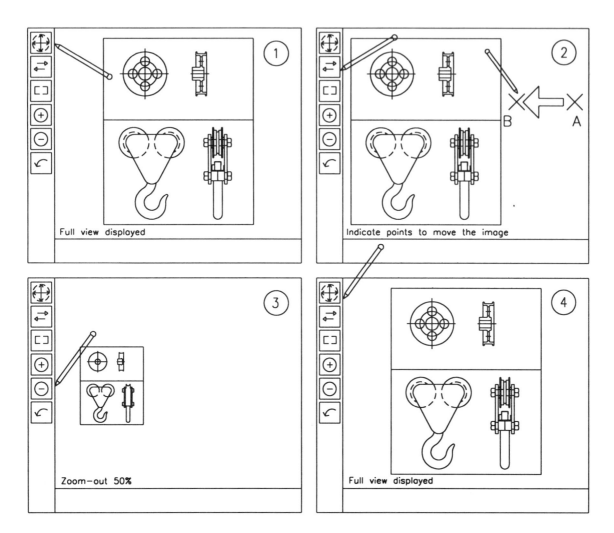

Fig. 4.4: *Views of the drawing are enlarged using view-display functions.*

Saving and Displaying Views

CADD allows you to store selected views and later display them back when required. When you are working with complex drawings, you need to display a number of views quickly. This function provides a convenient way to display selected views.

When you determine that you need to work on certain portions of a drawing frequently, you can store those views by giving them different names. To display any of the views, just reference the name of the view and it is instantly displayed.

Displaying Previous Views

CADD makes it easy to return to previously displayed views. Just click on the tool button designated to display the previous view and you are returned to the last view displayed. This feature is extremely useful because you often need to return to the portions of the drawing where you were recently working. By using this function, you can display all the previous views one by one by entering the function again and again. Some programs also allow you to display subsequent views after you return to previous views. You can go back and forth between all the views just by clicking on a tool button.

AutoCAD, MicroStation and Cadkey Terms

The following are the important terms used in leading CADD programs:
(The exact procedures vary from one program to another)

Task	AutoCAD	MicroStation	Cadkey
Displaying a full view	ZOOM: ALL ZOOM: EXTENTS	FIT VIEW	VIEW: ZOOM AUTOSCALE
Moving the view sideways	PAN	PAN VIEW	VIEW: PAN
Reducing the view	ZOOM (-)	ZOOM OUT	VIEW: MIN
Enlarging the view	ZOOM: WINDOW ZOOM (+)	ZOOM IN	VIEW: MAX
Saving and displaying views	VIEW: SAVE/DISPLAY	VIEW: SAVE/RECALL	DEFINE: DISPLAY VIEW
Displaying the last view	ZOOM: PREVIOUS	VIEW: PREVIOUS	VIEW: BACK 1

Important Tips:

• There are a number of additional view display techniques available in advanced CADD programs. One such technique is called real time pan and zoom that allows you to instantly manipulate the image by moving the cursor in a specific direction.

• Most CADD programs allow you to display multiple views side by side. The drawing area can be divided into different sections called viewports. You can display a different view in each viewport. This is particularly helpful when working with 3D drawings. For example, you can display a plan view in one viewport, elevation in another and a 3D view in another.

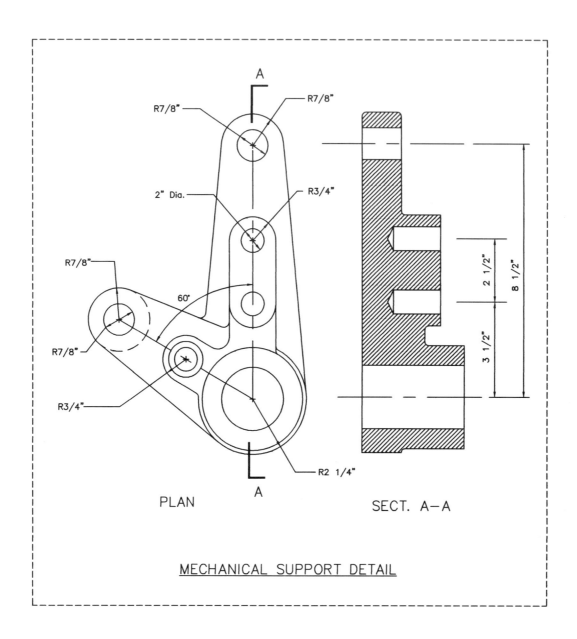

An example drawing created using CADD.

The Edit Functions

5

Contents

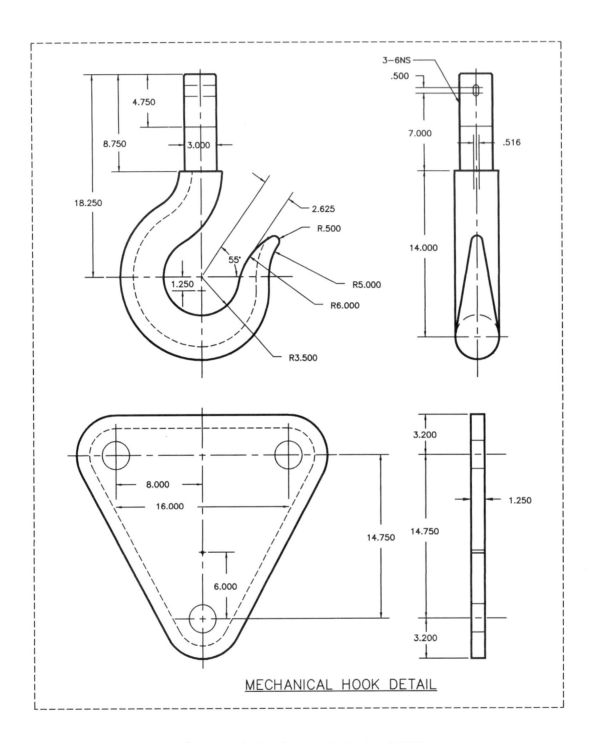

An example drawing created using CADD.

The Edit Functions

About this Chapter

This chapter focuses on CADD's editing module. The edit functions make CADD a very powerful drawing tool and contribute to significant timesaving in design and drafting. They provide a number of drawing shortcuts and enable you to fix drawing mistakes.

This chapter illustrates techniques by which you can manipulate drawing objects. It illustrates how to erase, move, copy, rotate, enlarge and reduce drawing objects. You will also learn how to use the edit functions as a drawing aid tool to make quick corrections.

The chapter ends with a read-through exercise that illustrates the basic steps to draw an engineer's office and an engineering complex plan.

Key Terms in this Chapter

Term	Description
Array	A set of multiple copies of selected objects.
Base point	A reference point used as a guide to move or copy objects.
Editing window	An imaginary rectangle formed by two diagonal points that is used to select drawing objects for editing.
Fillet	Joining lines or arcs at a corner.
Mirror	Creating a new object that is a mirror image of an original object.
Mirror-axis	An imaginary line along which the objects are mirrored.
Move	Moving selected objects from one place to another.
Stretch	Stretching a diagram in a specified direction.
Trim	Cutting drawing objects along a selected edge.

The Role of Edit Functions

The edit module provides great flexibility in changing CADD drawings. If you were to draw using only the drawing functions of CADD, it will probably take the same amount of time as it would on a drawing board. But CADD's editing functions make CADD a dynamic tool that results in significant timesaving.

Changes that may look extremely difficult on a drawing board can be easily accomplished with CADD. Even if you have to make a major change, chances are that you won't have to redraw it from scratch. You can manipulate the diagrams in a number of ways and may be able to rearrange the existing pieces of the drawing to fit the new shape.

The following are the basic capabilities of the edit module (See Fig. 5.1):

- Erasing drawing objects
- Moving drawing objects
- Copying drawing objects
- Changing the appearance of drawing objects

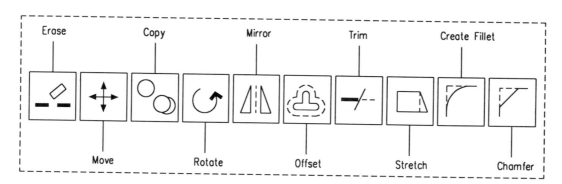

Fig. 5.1: *Common examples of editing tool buttons.*

Selecting Objects to Edit

In order to apply any of the edit functions, you need to select the drawing objects that need to be edited. CADD provides a number of methods by which you can select drawing objects. You can edit one object at a time, a group of objects, or the entire drawing at once.

The following are the basic methods for selecting drawing objects for editing: (The exact procedures vary from one program to another)

- Selecting objects one by one
- Selecting objects by enclosing them in a window
- Selecting objects using selection filters
- Making groups of selected objects

Selecting Objects One by One

When you need to edit only a few drawing objects, you can select them one by one. To select an object, use the pointing device to position the cursor on the object to be selected and then press the Enter button on the puck or mouse. You can select as many objects as you like by indicating them with the cursor one by one. The selected objects are highlighted with a distinct color or line type.

Selecting Objects by Enclosing them in a Window

When you need to select a number of drawing objects at once, you can select them by enclosing them in an editing window (an imaginary rectangle). You need to enter two diagonal points of the window and all the drawing objects enclosed within that window are selected. There are variations of this function available in many programs. For example, one function selects only the objects that are fully enclosed in the window, while another selects the objects that are just touching the window.

Selecting Objects using Selection Filters

Selection filters let you select objects that meet specified criteria. For example, you can select all drawing objects that are drawn on a specific layer or are drawn with a specific color. Advanced CADD programs even allow you to select similar objects according to their size, shape, line type, etc.

Making Groups of Selected Objects

CADD allows you to form groups of data in a drawing. All the objects selected within a group are edited together when any edit function is applied. The groups are usually formed to contain similar information. This is helpful when you need to edit the same drawing objects again and again. You form a group by selecting objects using any of the methods, and then giving the group a name. When you need to apply an edit function, specify the name of the group, and only the objects within that group are edited.

Erasing Drawing Objects

CADD provides a fast, accurate and convenient means of erasing drawings. Once you have entered the erase command, you are in the erase mode; any objects you select now will be instantly erased. You can use any method described above to select the objects.

Note:

The erase function is very powerful; it must be used with great caution. It can erase large amounts of information within seconds. If you make a mistake while erasing, be sure to take quick action. You can use the undo feature of CADD to disregard the effect of the last command.

Moving Drawing Objects

CADD allows you to move drawing objects within a drawing in a convenient manner. Unlike on a drawing board, you don't need to first erase and then redraw in a new place. You can simply rearrange the existing drawing objects, as you like. This is a very useful tool for analyzing design alternatives and making quick adjustments to drawings.

To move the objects, you need to enter the move function and select the objects to be moved. Enter a base point and a relocation point (destination point) and the selected objects are moved. The base point acts as an anchor for the selected objects and relocation point determines the new location of the selected objects. The objects are moved relative to the base point and the relocation point. Let's say you indicate the relocation point 4'-0" to the right of the base point. All the selected objects will be moved 4'-0" to the right.

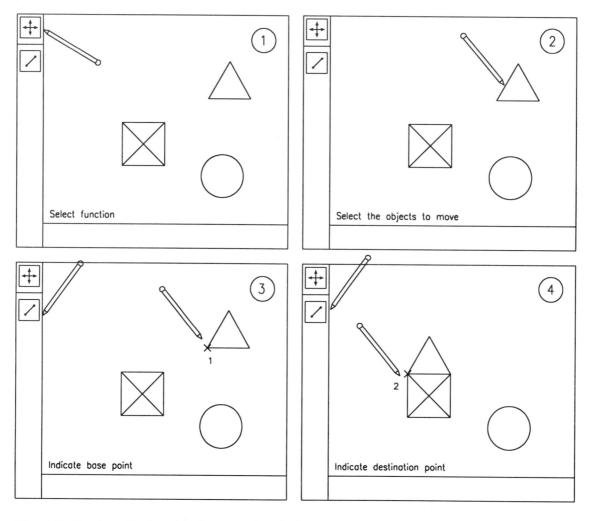

Fig. 5.2: *Moving objects using the move function.*

Fig. 5.2 (Screen 1) shows a square, a triangle and a circle randomly placed. The following steps illustrate how you can move the triangle on top of the square. For illustration purpose, only the tool buttons used in this exercise are shown.

Step	Action
1	(A) Click on the move tool button. (B) Select the triangle by placing cursor over it and then by pressing the Enter button on pointing device. The computer displays the prompt to select the base point. (C) Click on the end point object snap tool button. (D) Move the cursor near the end point of the triangle and press the Enter button on the pointing device.
2	The computer displays the prompt to enter the destination point. (A) Click on the end point object snap tool button. (B) Move the cursor over the end point of the square and press the Enter button on the pointing device. The triangle is moved on top of the square as shown.
3	Using the similar steps as described in step 1, enter the move function again and select the circle as the object to be moved. Indicate the base point at the center of the circle by using the center object snap too button.
4	Enter the relocation point at the mid-point of the diagonal of the square by using the mid-point object snap. The circle is moved exactly in the center of the square.

Copying Drawing Objects

CADD allows you to make quick and easy copies of existing drawing objects. You can copy individual drawing objects or the entire drawing all at once. You can even make multiple copies of drawing objects within seconds.

Using the copy function is quite similar to the way the move function is used. First, you need to select objects using any of the methods described earlier. Then you need to indicate a base point and a relocation (or destination) point. The copied objects are placed according to the relocation point.

Making Multiple Copies in a Rectangular Form

There are separate functions available in CADD that allow you to make multiple copies in a linear or rectangular form (commonly known as a rectangular array). You can make hundreds of copies within seconds. You don't need to enter a base point and a destination point. You just need to select the objects, specify how many rows and columns you need and the distance between them.

Fig. 5.3 illustrates how you can make multiple copies of a rectangular shape. To make five copies of the original shape as shown in Diagram A, you need to specify that the copies be made in two rows and three columns. Enter the distance between the rows as 3/4" and the distance between the columns as 1". Similarly, you can make 44 copies of an original by specifying 5 rows and 9 columns as shown in Diagram B.

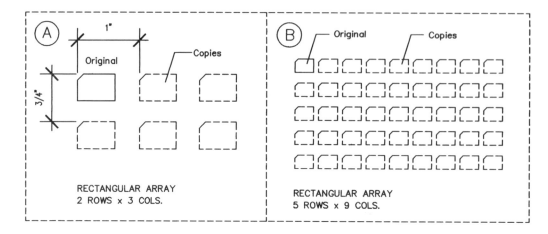

Fig. 5.3: *Making multiple copies of a diagram in rectangular form.*

Making Copies in a Circular Form

CADD allows you to make multiple copies of selected objects in a circular form (commonly known as a polar array). You need to enter the center point of array, number of copies required and the rotation angle. The center point of the array is a point around which the copies are arranged. The rotation angle determines the extent of the rotation, and the number of copies you specify are equally spaced between the rotation angle.

Fig. 5.4 illustrates how you can make multiple copies of a chair around a table. Diagram A shows the original. In Diagram B, seven copies of the chair are made to fit around half the table (rotation angle 180°). In Diagram C, the same number of chairs fit around three-quarters of the table (rotation angle 270°) and in Diagram D, they fit around the complete table (rotation angle 360°).

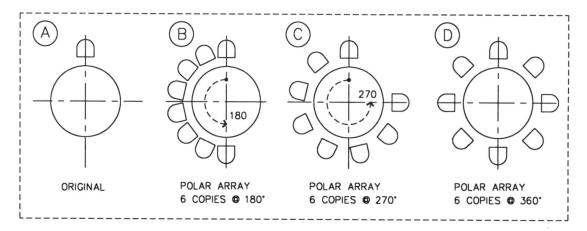

Fig. 5.4: *Copying a chair around a table.*

Changing Drawing Appearance

CADD allows you to change the appearance of drawing objects in a number of ways. You can change the line type, color, size and style of all the drawing objects. Using the editing functions of CADD, you can change almost every factor that defines a drawing object.

When you enter a command to change the drawing appearance, you are prompted to select the objects you want to change. You can select the objects using any of the methods discussed earlier. After the selection is made, you can specify what you want to change, and the selected objects are changed accordingly.

The edit functions allow you to do the following:

- Change line type, color and layer of drawing objects.
- Change the radius value of arcs and circles.
- Change major-axis, minor-axis and rotation angle of the ellipses.
- Change the thickness and flow of splines.
- Change the height, width, spacing, inclination, fonts and justification of text.
- Change the size, style, units, and accuracy of dimensions.
- Change the size and style of symbols, arrows, borders, and patterns.

Using Edit Functions as a Drawing-Aid Tool

The edit functions enable you to manipulate diagrams and make quick corrections in the following manners:

- Cutting drawing objects along an edge
- Drawing parallel lines and arcs
- Extending drawing objects to an edge
- Dividing an object into equal parts
- Making sharp and rounded corners
- Making chamfered corners
- Stretching a diagram
- Enlarging or reducing a diagram
- Rotating a diagram
- Mirroring a diagram

Cutting Drawing Objects Along an Edge

CADD allows you to erase drawing objects along a selected edge (this technique is often called trimming). When you use this function, you are prompted to select the drawing object that is to be used as the cutting edge and then select the objects that are to be erased along that edge.

Fig. 5.5 illustrates how you can erase lines along the edge of an arc. The diagram to the left (original) shows the lines crossing the arc. The second diagram shows that the arc is selected as the cutting edge. In the next diagram, the lines falling outside the arc are selected as the lines to be trimmed. The fourth diagram shows the result of trimming the lines along the arc.

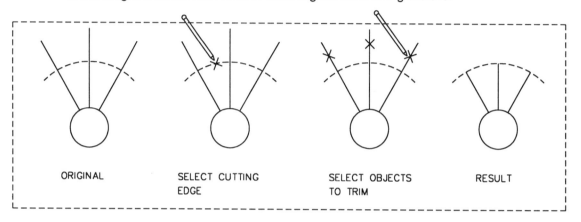

Fig. 5.5: *Trimming lines along an arc.*

Drawing Parallel Lines and Arcs

CADD allows you to draw parallel lines, arcs or splines using previously drawn objects as a reference. This technique is often called offsetting. To draw an offset parallel line, you need to select the drawing object to be used as a reference and then specify the distance and direction of the offset. A parallel drawing object is drawn at the specified distance.

Fig. 5.5 shows how you can draw multiple lines, arcs and splines using a single object as a reference. The dark lines shown in the diagram represent the original drawing objects. The rest of the drawing objects are drawn as an offset of the original. When the first offset is drawn, it can be used to draw the next parallel drawing object.

Note: When drawing an offset to the inside of an arc, you cannot enter a greater value for the offset than the radius of the selected arc. Such an arc is not possible to draw and the computer displays an error message.

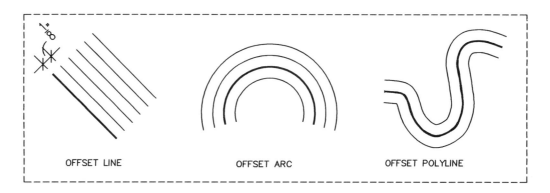

Fig. 5.6: *Drawing offset parallel lines, arcs and splines.*

Extending Drawing Objects to an Edge

CADD allows you to extend lines to a selected drawing object. Often you need to extend lines to construct a drawing and to fix any graphical errors. To extend lines, you need to select an edge to which the lines should extend and then select the lines to be extended. Fig. 5.7 shows how you can extend a number of lines to an edge formed by a line and arcs.

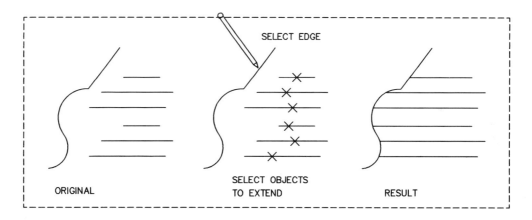

Fig. 5.7: *A number of lines are extended to an edge.*

Dividing an Object into Equal Parts

CADD allows you to place dividing marks on a drawing object such as a line, arc, ellipse or spline. To use this command, you need to select an object and specify how many divisions are required. This function places markers at equal distances on the drawing object.

Fig. 5.8 shows how you can divide an arc, an ellipse, a line and a spline into equal parts. It takes only seconds to place the dividing markers and you don't need to do any calculations. The divisions are accurate to the last fraction and the results can be used for any calculation.

Note: The markers drawn are only for reference, they do not break the drawing object. You can erase the markers when you are finished using them.

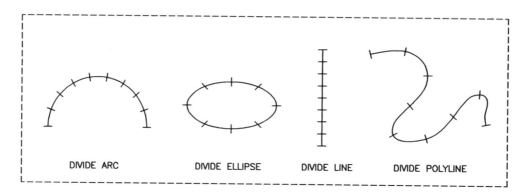

DIVIDE ARC   DIVIDE ELLIPSE   DIVIDE LINE   DIVIDE POLYLINE

Fig. 5.8: *An arc, an ellipse, a line and a spline are divided into equal parts.*

Making Chamfered Corners

CADD allows you to make a chamfered corner between two lines. It works quite like the fillet command. When you enter the chamfer command, you are prompted to select the lines that are to be chamfered and enter a chamfer distance. The chamfer distance determines the size of the chamfer. Fig. 5.9 shows how you can make a chamfered corner between two lines that are set apart.

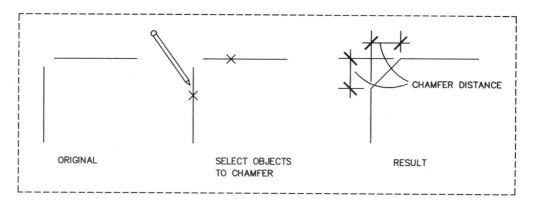

ORIGINAL   SELECT OBJECTS TO CHAMFER   RESULT

Fig. 5.9: *A chamfered corner is made between two lines.*

Making Sharp and Rounded Corners

CADD allows you to make fine corners of any two lines or arcs. This technique, often called filleting, is the quickest way to join the missing corners of lines and arcs. With this function active, to make a corner all you need to do is select the lines or arcs that have missing corners. CADD automatically extends or shortens the selected objects to form a corner. You can also specify whether you want a sharp corner or a rounded corner.

Fig. 5.10 shows how you can join the missing corners of lines and arcs. Diagram A shows how to make a sharp corner of two lines that are set apart. Diagram B shows how to make rounded corners between lines and arcs. When making a rounded corner you can specify the radius of the arc that is to be used to create the fillet.

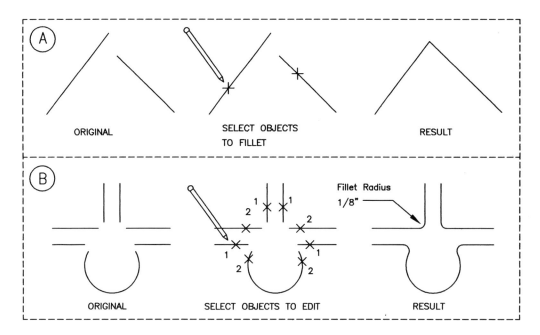

Fig. 5.10: *Making sharp and rounded corners of lines and arcs.*

Stretching Diagrams

CADD allows you to quickly change the size of diagrams by stretching lines, arcs, splines, etc. This function is very helpful to make quick alterations to drawings. To use the stretch function, you need to select the drawing objects to be stretched and specify the distance and direction of stretching.

Fig. 5.11 shows how you can stretch a rectangular-shaped diagram to make it longer. The objects to be stretched are selected by enclosing them in an editing window formed by points 1 and 2. The diagram is stretched in the horizontal direction by 1/2".

Note: When dimensions are stretched, the program updates the dimension values automatically. When text and symbols are stretched, their appearance remains unchanged but they are relocated. When only one end of an arc is stretched, it may deform the shape of the arc.

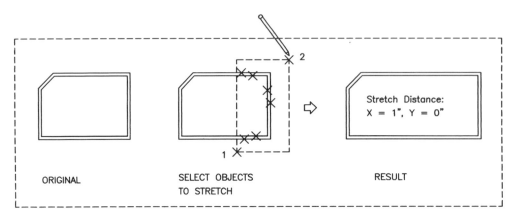

Fig. 5.11: *A diagram is stretched in the horizontal direction.*

Enlarging or Reducing Diagrams

CADD allows you to enlarge or reduce diagrams in a convenient manner. To enlarge or reduce diagrams, you need to select the objects and enter a scale factor. The scale factor determines by how much the diagrams are to be reduced or enlarged.

Example: To reduce a 10'x20' square to a 5'x10' square, you would need to enter a scale factor of 0.5. Similarly, to enlarge the diagram to twice its original size, you would need to enter a scale factor of 2. You can precisely reduce or enlarge the diagrams by entering an exact scale factor. Fig. 5.12 shows how you might enlarge a portion of a diagram four times to show it in more detail.

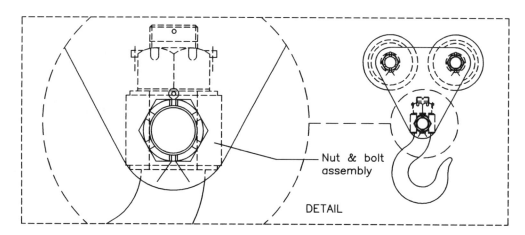

Fig. 5.12: *A part of the diagram is enlarged to four times the original size.*

Rotating the Diagrams

CADD allows you to rotate selected drawing objects to a specified angle. To rotate, you need to select the drawing objects, enter a reference point (or base point) and the rotation angle. The base point acts as a pivot point around which the objects are rotated. The rotation angle determines by how much the objects will be rotated and in which direction.

Fig. 5.13 illustrates the ways you can rotate a drawing 45° by indicating different base points. The diagram on the left shows how the drawing is rotated when the base point is entered in the middle of the drawing. The diagram in the middle shows the rotation when the base point is entered at a corner. The diagram on the right shows what happens when the base point is entered away from the drawing.

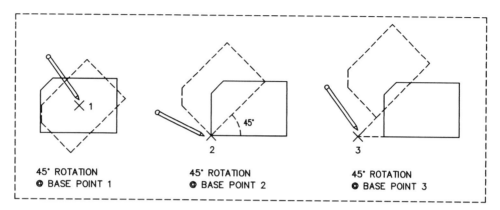

Fig. 5.13: *A diagram is rotated at 45°.*

Mirroring the Diagrams

CADD allows you to create mirror images of selected drawing objects. This capability is very useful when you want to draw something that is symmetrical on both sides. You need to draw only one half of the drawing; the rest of the drawing can be completed using the mirror function. To make a mirror image, you need to select the objects to be mirrored and indicate a mirror axis. The mirror axis is an imaginary line along which the diagram is mirrored. Fig. 5.14 illustrates how you can draw a complete flange drawing from only half the drawing.

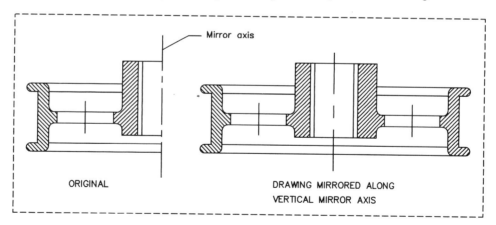

Fig. 5.14: *Half of the flange drawing is mirrored to make a complete flange diagram.*

Steps to Draw an Engineer's Office

Here is an exercise to draw a plan of a room called engineer's office. The engineer's office is 19 feet, 6 inches long and 13 feet, 6 inches wide. It has a chamfered corner on one side and has a door in the opposite corner. We will accurately draw this plan using drawing, editing and view-display functions.

The exercise is completed in 20 steps (Fig. 5.16 to 5.21). First, we will complete the plan of a single room (Fig. 5.16 to Fig. 5.19). We will use this plan to make a 4-unit office block as shown in Screen 20 Fig. 5.20. Later, we will describe how to use this office block to make a complete engineering complex as shown in Fig. 5.22.

Note:

The objective of this exercise is to give a general overview of working with edit functions. The illustrations show only the basic steps required to complete the drawing. The exact procedures vary from one program to another.

For illustration purpose, only the tool buttons required in the exercise are shown. Fig. 5.15 shows some of the examples.

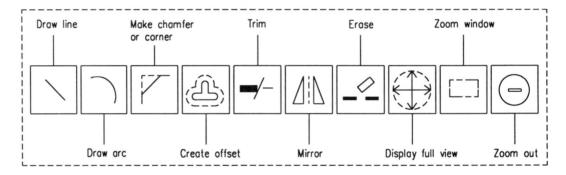

Fig. 5.15: *The tool buttons used to complete the engineer's office plan.*

The following are the basic steps (Fig. 5.16) to draw the outline of the engineer's office:

Step	Action
1	Click on the line tool button and draw a horizontal and a vertical line. The lines don't need to be exact and can be drawn roughly as shown on screen 1.
2	Click on the offset tool button. When the computer displays prompts, select the horizontal line as the reference and enter the offset distance as 13'-6". This draws a horizontal parallel line. Similarly draw a vertical parallel line at 19'-6" distance. Note: The dimensions shown are for illustration purpose only.
3	Click on the chamfer tool button and enter the chamfer distance to be zero. When the computer displays the prompt to select lines, select one vertical and one horizontal line that roughly make a corner. This forms a sharp corner between the lines. Repeat this task for three corners of the diagram as shown.
4	Click on the chamfer tool button and enter the chamfer distance as 3'-0". Select the two lines on the upper left corner and a 3'-0" chamfer is formed as shown.

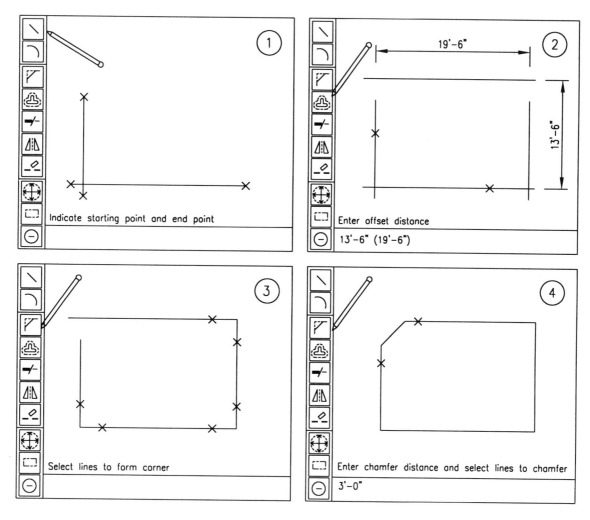

Fig. 5.16: *Drawing an outline of the engineer's office plan.*

The following are the basic steps (Fig. 5.17) to draw the walls of the engineer's office:

Step	Action
5	Click on the offset tool button and select any line to create an offset. Enter the offset distance 6" and enter the direction of the offset on the outside of the diagram. A parallel line is drawn, which represents the wall of the engineer's office. Repeat this step for all the sides of the plan.
6	Click on the zoom-window tool button and indicate points 1 & 2 as the corners of the window to be magnified.
7	A magnified view of the chamfered corner is displayed. As shown, the parallel lines created don't make sharp corners at the ends. Use the form corner tool button to form sharp corners. Repeat this step for all the corners of the plan.
8	Zoom out to display the entire drawing.

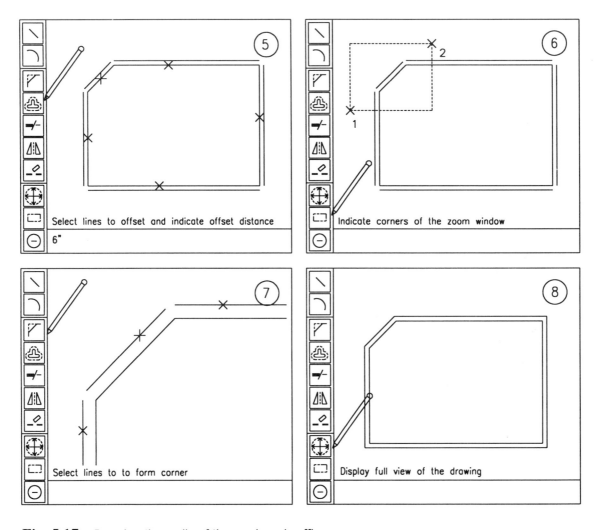

Fig. 5.17: *Drawing the walls of the engineer's office.*

The following are the basic steps (Fig. 5.18) to create a door opening in the wall:

Step	Action
9	Magnify bottom right corner of the plan using the zoom window tool.
10	Click on the offset tool button and select the vertical line on the right as a reference line. Enter the offset distance 1'-0" and indicate the direction of offset to the left. A vertical parallel line is drawn to the left. Use this line as a reference and create another offset at 3'-0" distance to the left.
11	Click on the trim tool button and select the vertical lines as the trimming edges. Select two horizontal lines as the lines to be trimmed and they are erased in the middle. This makes the door opening.
12	Click on the trim tool button again and trim two vertical lines in the same manner to form a clear door opening as shown on screen 13.

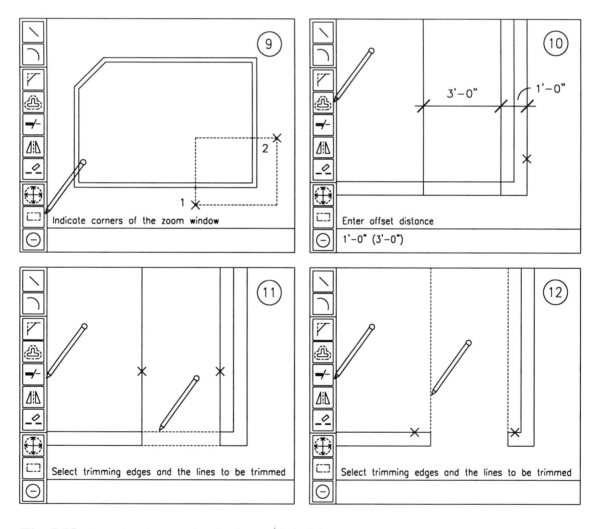

Fig. 5.18: *Marking the opening for the symbol of door.*

The following are the basic steps (Fig. 5.19) to complete the engineer's office plan:

Step	Action
13	Click on the line tool button and draw a 3'-0" long vertical line from point 1 to point 2.
14	Click on the arc tool button and draw an arc using the center point and starting point and end point method. Indicate 1 as the center point of the arc, 2 as the starting point and 3 as the end point. This completes the symbol of the door.
15	Zoom out to display the entire plan diagram. This completes the engineer's office plan diagram. We will use this diagram to make a 2-unit office block as shown on screen 19. Later, we will use this 2-unit office block to make a 4-unit office as shown on screen 24.
16	Click on the offset tool button and draw a parallel line at 2'-6" distance below the horizontal line of the office wall.

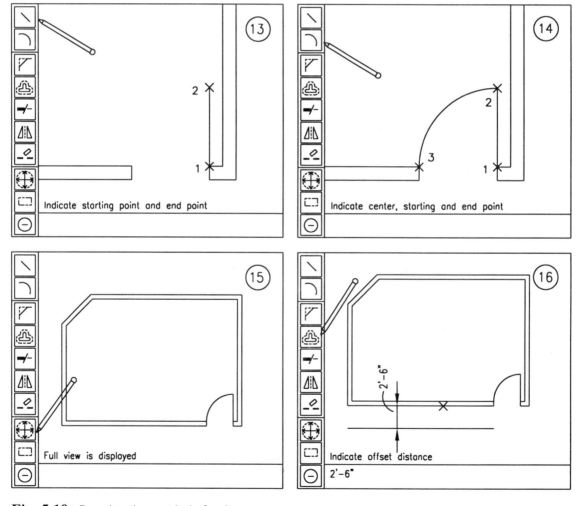

Fig. 5.19: *Drawing the symbol of a door.*

The following are the basic steps (Fig. 5.20) to make a two-unit office block:

Step	Action
17	Reduce the image size to approximately half using the view-display functions.
18	Click on the mirror tool button and select the engineer's office plan by enclosing it in the editing window formed by points 1 and 2. Make sure the entire office plan is selected.
19	When the screen displays the prompt to indicate mirror axis, select the horizontal line as the mirror axis. A mirrored copy of the office plan is created as shown.
20	Click on the erase tool button, place the cursor over the horizontal line and press the Enter button on the cursor. The horizontal line is erased. Note: The horizontal line was drawn just for reference to create a mirror copy. Since the line was drawn at 2'-6" distance from the first office, this has placed the second office at the same distance from the line. This has created a 5'-0" passage way between the two offices.

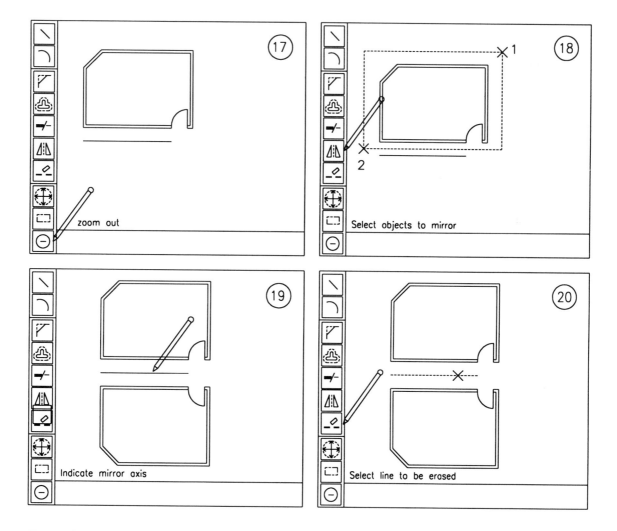

Fig. 5.20: *Mirroring the engineer's office plan.*

The following are the basic steps (Fig. 5.21) to create a four-unit office block:

Step	Action
21	Click on the mirror tool button again and select both the offices by enclosing them in the editing window formed by points 1 & 2.
22	Display a magnified view of the plan near the door area.
23	Indicate the mirror axis by selecting the exact corners of the office plan at point 1 and 2. A mirrored copy of the offices is made.
24	Display a full view of the plan. This completes a four-unit office block. We will use the office block to complete the engineering complex.

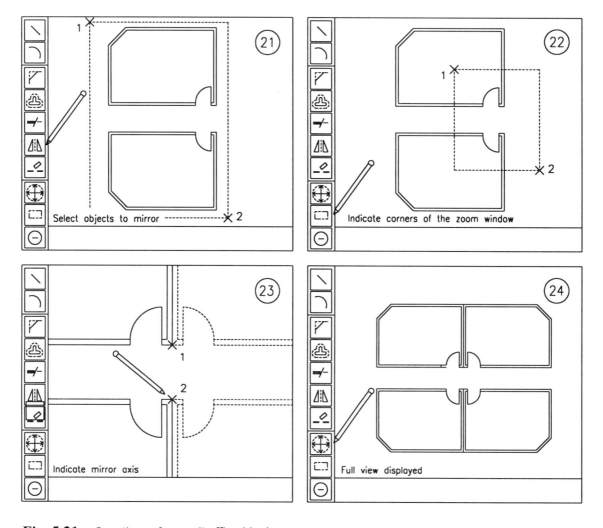

Fig. 5.21: *Creating a four-unit office block.*

Steps to Complete the Engineering Complex

You can use the engineering office unit plan drawn in the previous exercise (Fig. 5.20) to complete the engineering complex as shown in Fig. 5.21. The engineering complex has two major blocks: the engineering block and the administrative block. Each block has four identical office units. The office units are connected together with a 50'-0"X 50'-0" octagonal court in the middle. The complex has some landscaping and parking around it.

The following is the brief description to complete the engineering complex (Fig. 5.21).

Step	Action
1	Draw a 50'-0"x 50'-0" square with diagonal lines. Align the four-unit office block to the left of the square. You can use the move function to perfectly center the plan on the left side of the square.
2	Use the array function to make 4 identical office units around the square. Use the intersection of the square diagonals as the center point of the array. Draw an octagon connecting the end points of the office units. Create a second to the inside by using the offset function. Erase the square and the diagonal lines.
3	Use the copy function to make a copy of the entire diagram finished in step 2 and place it next to it as shown. Label different areas of the complex using the text function. Add symbols of cars and trees to complete the drawing.

Important Tips:

- It gets easier to multiply and manipulate information once a certain portion of the drawing is completed. It took quite some effort to create the first unit of the engineer's office, but it took only a few steps to multiply it to make a two-unit office block and then a four-unit office block, and then the entire engineering complex.

- There are a number of ready-made symbols available in CADD that can be instantly added to a drawing. Symbol libraries are available from independent vendors as well. To learn about symbols libraries, refer to Chapter 9 "Maximizing CADD."

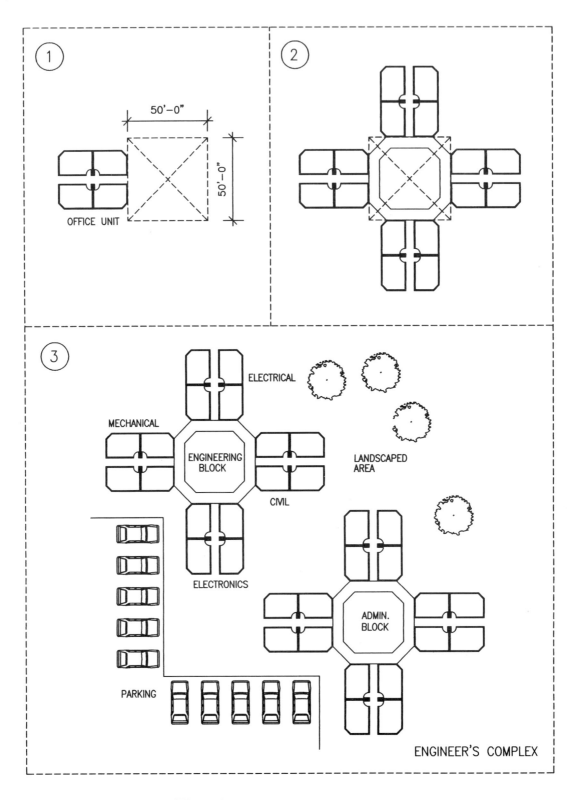

Fig. 5.21: *The engineer's complex.*

AutoCAD, MicroStation and Cadkey Terms

The following are the important terms used in leading CADD programs:
(The exact procedures vary from one program to another)

Function	AutoCAD	MicroStation	Cadkey
Erasing drawing objects	ERASE	DELETE ELEMENT	EDIT: DELETE/ ENTITIES
Moving drawing objects	MOVE	MOVE ELEMENT	X-FORM: DELTA/ MOVE
Copying drawing objects	COPY	COPY ELEMENT DUPLICATE	X-FORM DELTA/COPY
Making multiple copies in a rectangular fashion	ARRAY: RECTANGULAR	ARRAY RECTANGULAR	X-FORM: DELTA COPY/CHAIN
Making copies in a circular fashion	ARRAY: POLAR	ARRAY POLAR	X-FORM: CIRCULAR ARRAY
Changing the appearance of drawing objects	CHANGE PROPERTIES	CHANGE ATTRIBUTES	CHANGE ATTRIBUTES
Cutting drawing objects along an edge	TRIM	TRIM ELEMENTS	MODIFY: TRIM
Drawing parallel lines	OFFSET	COPY:PARALLEL/ DISTANCE	CREATE: LINE/ PARALLEL
Extending drawing objects to an edge	EXTEND	EXTEND ELEMENT	MODIFY: TRIM
Dividing drawing objects into equal parts	DIVIDE	CONSTRUCT POINT	CREATE: POINT
Making rounded corners	FILLET: RADIUS	FILLET: CONSTRUCT CIRCULAR FILLET	CREATE: FILLET/ARC
Making chamfered corners	CHAMFER	CHAMFER	FILLET: CHAMFER
Stretching diagrams	STRETCH	EXTEND LINE	X-FORM: BOX/ MOVE
Enlarging or reducing diagrams	SCALE	SCALE ORIGINAL SCALE COPY	X-FORM/SCALE
Rotating diagrams	ROTATE	SPIN ORIGINAL SPIN COPY	X-FORM/ROTATE
Mirroring diagrams	MIRROR	MIRROR COPY	X-FORM/MIRROR

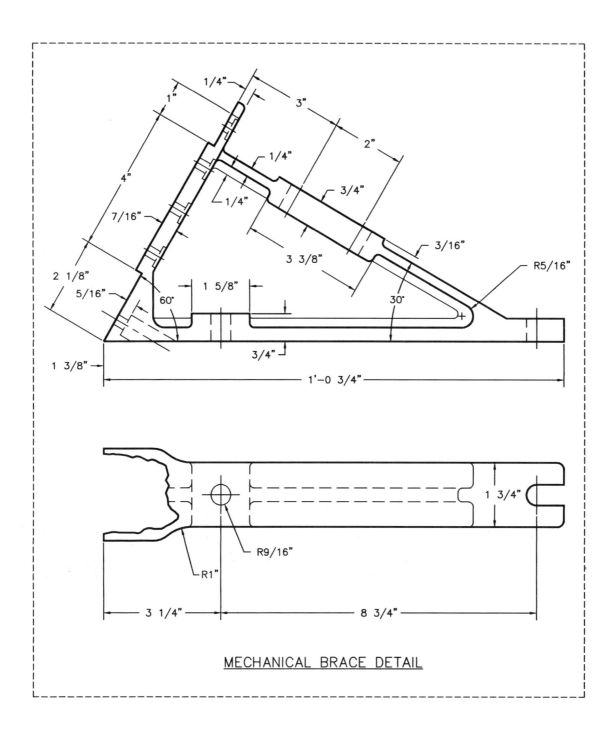

MECHANICAL BRACE DETAIL

An example drawing created using CADD.

Working With Layers

Contents

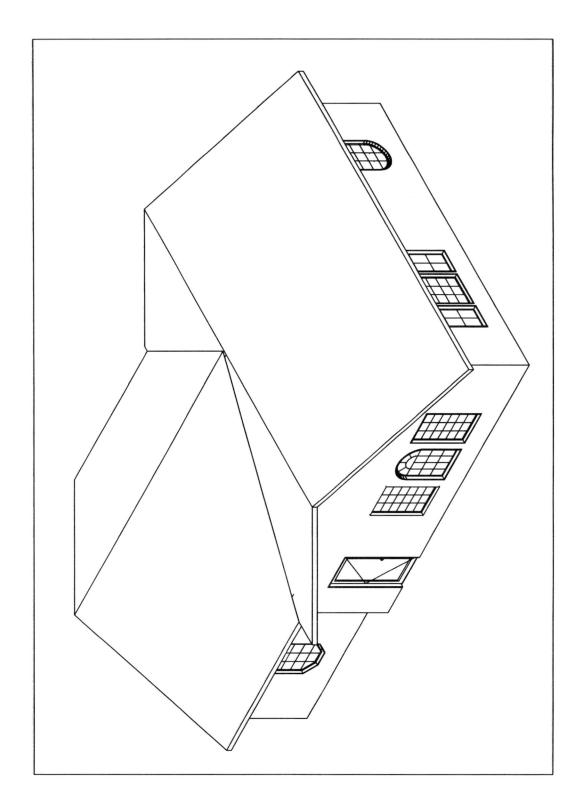

An example 3D drawing created using CADD: Courtesy Eaglepoint Software.

Working With Layers

Key Terms in this Chapter

Term	Description
Composite drawing	A drawing that contains multiple drawings created with the help of CADD layers.
Layer or level	A transparent surface created within a drawing.
Layer color	A color assigned to a layer.
Layer off	Making the drawing objects on a layer invisible.
Layer on	Making the drawing objects on a layer visible.
Layer line type	A line type assigned to a layer.
Locking a layer	Making the drawing objects on a layer permanent and non-editable.
Macro	A recorded set of instructions that can be used to repeat a task.

The Concept of Layers in CADD

Layers are imaginary transparent surfaces that can be created within a CADD drawing. You can draw on these imaginary surfaces and group drawing objects on different layers (Fig. 6.1). This helps to organize CADD drawings and makes editing much easier. You can turn the layers on or off to view or edit specific objects. When you turn a layer off, the objects on that layer disappear from the screen; when you turn it back on, they are displayed. Using layers enables you to control the display of specific information on the screen by turning a combination of layers on or off.

You may create dozens of layers in a drawing to segregate drawing objects. You may create separate layers to show dimensions, hatch patterns and for any drawing objects that are different in nature. This provides a great convenience in editing drawings. When drawings are complex and a number of drawing objects are overlapping, you can turn off the unwanted layers. This makes it much easier to select the desired objects for editing. When you are finished editing, you can turn the layers back on.

Layers are commonly used in professional architecture and engineering drawings. Architects and engineers often need to coordinate different engineering services in a plan. They can illustrate different engineering services on the same drawing using different layers. This helps them understand how one engineering service relates to another.

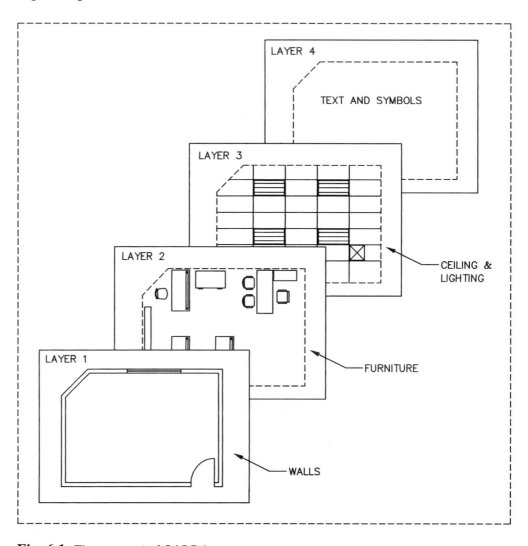

Fig. 6.1: *The concept of CADD layers.*

Creating Layers for an Engineer's Office

Fig. 6.1 illustrates how you can organize an engineer's office diagram in several layers. You can place walls and partitions on one layer, furniture and equipment on another, and so on for text, symbols, and construction lines, etc. You can also create a separate layer to show the ceiling and lighting plan, floor finish plan, or any other drawing objects that you want to include in the drawing.

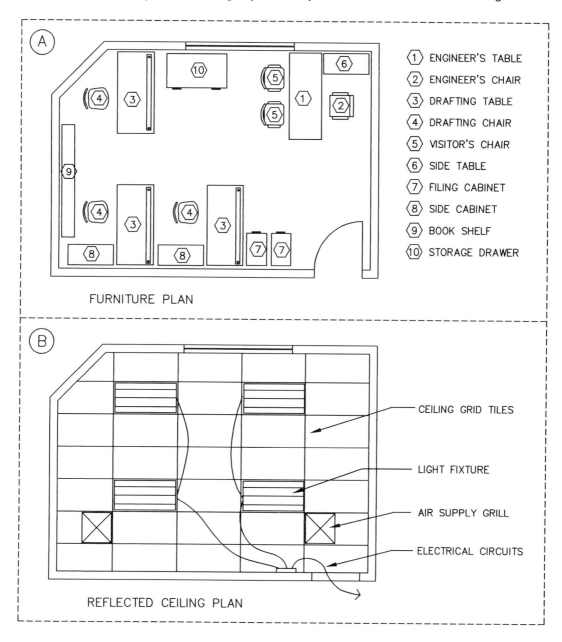

Fig. 6.2: *Different drawings are created with the use of layers.*

Fig. 6.2 shows how you can display a furniture plan and a reflected ceiling plan from this multi-layered drawing. When you need to display the furniture layout as shown in illustration A, you can turn on the wall and furniture layers, and turn off the rest. When you need to display the ceiling and lighting plan (Diagram B), you can turn on only the ceiling and the wall layers. You can turn the relevant text and symbol layers on and off as required.

Note:

Layers are given specific characteristics that distinguish them from each other. Each layer has a specific color and line type. Whatever you draw on a layer is drawn with that color and line type. This color coding helps to identify which drawing objects are placed on which layer.

The Tools to Work with Layers

CADD provides a number of tools that allow you to work efficiently with layers. Most programs use a layer control window that allows you to manage all aspects of working with layers.

The following are the basic tools for working with layers:

- Creating new layers
- Setting a layer current
- Changing color and line type for a layer
- Turning layers on or off
- Locking and unlocking layers

Creating New Layers

CADD allows you to create a number of layers in a drawing. To create a new layer you need to enter the name of the layer and assign a color and line type to it. The layer name should reflect the kind of information it contains.

Most companies follow standard guidelines in naming layers and placing specific information on specific layers. This allows CADD users to efficiently coordinate information. Professional institutes such as the American Institute of Architects (AIA) and the American Institute of Engineers (AIE) have developed standard naming conventions for layers that are commonly used by CADD professionals.

The following are some examples of layer names developed by the American Institute of Architects (AIA):

Layer name	Description
A-CLNG-GRID	Ceiling grid
A-WALL-EXTR	Exterior full height walls
E-LITE-CLNG	Ceiling-mounted light fixtures
E-LITE-CIRC	Lighting circuits
G-ANNO-NOTE	General notes and general remarks
G-ANNO-TTLB	Border and title block line work
I-FURN-TABL	Tables
I-FURN-SEAT	Chairs, sofas, etc.

AIA layers constitute hundreds of names that accommodate all disciplines of the building trade. The first letter of the layer name identifies a building trade. For example, A for architectural, E for electrical, I for interior design, S for structural, L for landscape and G for general drawings. There are dozens of layer names established for each engineering discipline.

For more information, visit the web site of the American Institute of Architects at http://www.aia.org/.

Facility Information Council (FIC) of the National Institute of Building Sciences (NIBS) has taken the initiative to develop universal CADD standards including layer names. For information visit their web site at: http://www.nationalcadstandard.org/.

Setting a Layer to Current

When you need to work on a specific layer, you must set that layer to be current by selecting it in the layer control window (Fig. 6.3). When a layer is set current, whatever you draw is drawn on that layer. The current layer name or number is displayed in the status bar.

Let's say you want to add some new furniture to the diagram as shown in Fig. 6.2. In order to maintain consistency, the new furniture must be drawn on the same layer as the existing furniture. You can set the furniture layer as the current layer. Subsequently, all the drawing work will be drawn on the furniture layer and should appear in the same color as the other furniture. If the color or line type is different, you may be working on the wrong layer.

Changing Color and Line Type of Layers

You can change the color and line type of layers at any time. When you change the color and line type of layers, all the drawing objects on that layer are displayed with the new color and line type. You can instantly make adjustments to colors and line types by selecting the layer from the layer control window (Fig. 6.3, 6.4) and choosing a color and line type for the layer.

Note: The colors used in a CADD drawing represent certain line weights and pen numbers when the drawings are plotted. More on colors and line weights is discussed in Chapter 8, "Printing and Plotting."

Turning Layers On or Off

You can turn any number of layers on or off by selecting them from the layer control window. To turn on a layer, highlight it in the layer control window and press the ON button (Fig. 6.3, 6.4). Similarly, you can turn the layers off when needed.

Turning layers on and off provides a great convenience for drawing and editing, as well as for plotting. To plot selected layers, simply turn off the rest of the layers. When drawing and editing, it is also a good idea to turn off unwanted layers, particularly when there is a lot of information on the screen. This speeds up the display process.

Locking and Unlocking Layers

Most CADD programs allow you to assign a lock or unlock status to layers. If a layer is locked, it means that you can't erase, move, or copy anything on that layer. To erase any drawing object from that layer, you must first unlock it. If there are certain drawing objects that are of a permanent nature and you don't want to run the risk of accidentally erasing or moving them, you can lock that layer.

Are Layers Absolutely Necessary?

Layers are not absolutely necessary, however they provide a convenient way to manage information in CADD drawings. For example, in the engineer's office example, without the help of this function you may have to create separate drawings to show the furniture plan, lighting plan, etc. With the help of layers, you can create just one composite drawing. The composite drawing can contain all the plans. It makes it easier to correlate information from one plan to another.

For complex drawings, layers are a must because they make editing much easier. Often you need to select only specific drawing objects for editing, and the use of layers makes its very easy to select them.

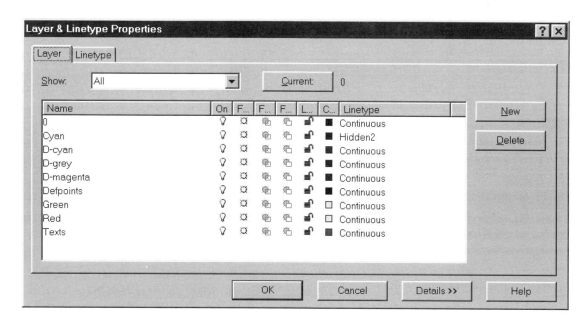

Fig. 6.3: *The layer control window used in AutoCAD.*

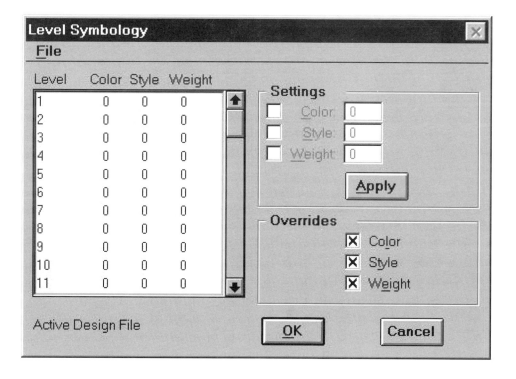

Fig. 6.4: *The layer control window used in MicroStation.*

Important Tips:

- When working on an existing drawing, you must first examine how many layers exist in the drawing and which layer contains what information. If you start working on a drawing that has certain layers turned off, you may not be aware of the hidden data.

- When layers are turned off, the drawing objects on those layers are not affected by the use of any edit function. Be careful when using move or copy functions when some layers are turned off. You may copy over or move a drawing that is turned off. Later on, When you turn all the layers on, drawing objects may be overlapped or unaligned.

- Most CADD programs allow you to create customized macros that can make working with layers a snap. You can write a macro that can instantly turn on or off a combination of layers. For example, you can write a macro named FP (Furniture Plan) that automatically displays the layers required for a furniture plan. Thereafter, when you enter the word FP on the keyboard, it will automatically display the furniture plan. You can create dozens of macros to display specific diagrams.

AutoCAD, MicroStation and Cadkey Terms

The following are the important terms used in leading CADD programs:
(The exact procedures vary from one program to another)

Function	AutoCAD	MicroStation	Cadkey
Creating new layers	LAYER: NEW	LEVEL: NAME	LEVELS: DISCRIPTOR
Setting a layer current	LAYER: CURRENT	LEVEL: ACTIVE	LEVELS: SET ACTIVE
Changing color and line type of layers	LAYER: COLOR/LINETYPE	LEVEL: SYMBOLOGY	Not applicable
Turning layers on or off	LAYER: ON/OFF	SET LEVELS: ON/OFF	LEVELS: ADD/REMOVE
Locking and unlocking layers	LAYER: LOCK/UNLOCK	LOCK: LEVEL	LEVEL: MASK

Introduction to 3D

7

Contents

Contents

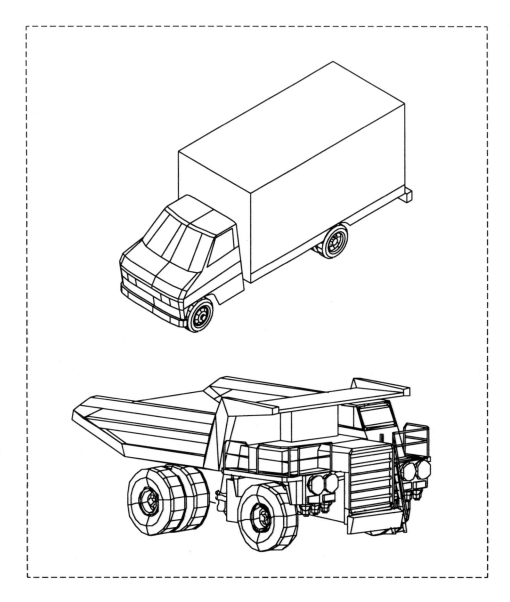

An example drawing created using CADD.

Introduction to 3D

About this Chapter

This chapter introduces you to the general principles of 3D (three-dimensional) drawing that are commonly used in CADD. It describes how to make use of simple 2D functions to create a 3D effect, as well as how to create actual 3D models. You will learn how to measure distances in 3D, how to enter 3D coordinates and how to draw 3D shapes.

This chapter describes a number of 3D drawing techniques that are commonly used by CADD professionals. You will learn how to extrude 3D objects from simple 2D shapes, how to take advantage of 3D ready-made objects and how to make the views look realistic.

You will also learn how to display 3D views of a model from different angles.

Although the actual working of 3D CADD varies from program to program, the principles described here can be applied to most programs.

Key Terms in this Chapter

Term	Description
3D coordinates	The mode of measurement used to specify the length, width and height of objects created by 3D modeling.
3D modeling	A CADD capability that allows you to draw objects as physical objects having length, width and height.
Isometric	A view of an object tilted at 30° on both sides.
Linear extrusion	A 3D technique that allows you to form 2D shapes into 3D shapes along a linear path.
Oblique view	A view of an object drawn by taking parallel projections from an elevation.
Perspective	A view of an object showing true angles as they would appear from a specific point.
Radial extrusion	A 3D technique that allows you to form 2D shapes into 3D shapes along a circular path.
Viewpoint	The point from where a 3D model is viewed.

Why 3D?

3D capabilities allow you to draw pictorial views such as isometrics, oblique views and perspectives. The views drawn with CADD have a number of advantages as compared to views drawn on a drawing board. The views drawn with CADD are very accurate and provide a lot of flexibility in terms of editing and display. You can rotate a model on the screen just like an actual model, and display views from different angles.

Designers often use 3D to visualize designs and to make presentations. It helps them understand how an object will appear from different angles. Using additional rendering programs can further enhance the drawings.

Although working with 3D CADD programs is quite complex, it is worth the extra effort to make use of them. Many users never take the time to learn the 3D capabilities of CADD. This can be a major disadvantage because the full potential of CADD is never explored.

Pictorial Views Concept

How do we create 3D views on paper or on a computer screen, which are only two-dimensional media? Is an isometric or perspective 2D or 3D?

The views that we draw on two-dimensional media are a 2D representation of 3D images. We create isometrics and perspectives on paper by drawing objects as they would appear from a specific angle and distance. The same concept is used in CADD to draw pictorial views.

There are two distinct ways to draw 3D views with CADD: You can draw views using simple 2D functions or using CADD's special 3D functions.

The 2D functions allow you to draw views just like on a drawing board. You can draw a view using lines, arcs, or other 2D objects. This is the quickest method to draw simple isometric and oblique views. However, a view created this way is static; just like a view created on a drawing board. If you need to view the object from a different angle, you will have to draw it again from scratch.

CADD provides special 3D functions that allow you to create 3D drawings that are true representations of an actual model. These drawings can be viewed from any angle just like a physical model. That is why 3D CADD drawings are called 3D models.

The major distinction between a 2D drawing and a 3D model is that a 2D drawing is defined only with two coordinates (X and Y). A 3D model is defined with three coordinates (X, Y and Z). The Z-coordinate determines the height of an object. To make a 3D model, you need to consider all the objects of the model in 3D space and enter the X, Y and Z coordinates for all drawing objects.

3D modeling is described later in this chapter. Let's begin with simple oblique and isometric examples.

Oblique Views

Oblique views are the simplest form of the pictorial views that can be drawn by using parallel projection lines from an elevation (see Fig. 7.1). There are standards established to draw oblique views at specific angles. A common standard used is to draw an oblique view by projecting lines at 45°. To measure depth along a 45° angle, you need to scale it down by 3/4 or 1/2 of the actual distance. For example, if the actual depth of the object is 1'-0", you measure 9" or 6". The 3/4 scale factor creates an effect as if the object is viewed from a slightly higher angle than the 1/2 scale factor.

To draw an oblique view with CADD, you need to follow the same steps as used on a drawing board. The following are the basic steps to complete the diagram shown in Fig. 7.1:

Step	Action
1	Draw the elevation of the object.
2	Draw parallel projection lines at 45° angle and measure the depth along the projection lines by scaling it down to show appropriate depth.
3	Draw the elevation as it appears at the end of the projection lines.
4	Draw more projection lines to show the thickness at the back, and complete the diagram.

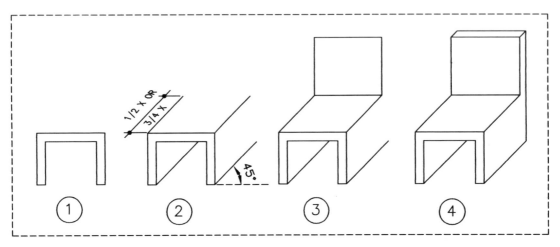

Fig. 7.1: *Drawing an oblique view.*

Isometric Views

Isometric views are more realistic than oblique views. The object appears to be tilted at a 30° angle on both sides (see Fig. 7.2). An isometric is defined by three planes called isoplanes: top isoplane, right isoplane and left isoplane.

On a drawing board, we use a 30° triangle to draw the three planes of an isometric. The same principle is applied in CADD with the help of various functions. The right isoplane is drawn with 30° and 90° angles, the left isoplane with 150° and 90° angles and the top plane with 30° and 150° angles. All distances are measured using 1:1 scale (actual size) to show depth, width and height. You can use simple 2D functions and draw lines at specific angles to complete an isometric. Polar coordinates are particularly helpful to measure distances along an angle.

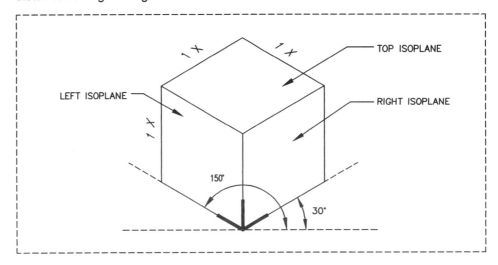

Fig. 7.2: *The isometric drawing concept.*

Steps to Draw an Isometric

The following are the basic steps to complete the diagram shown in Fig. 7.3:

Step	Action
1	Enter the Line command and enter the starting point of line anywhere in the drawing area (point A).
2	Draw a line from point A to B using polar coordinates. The line is to be 30'-0" long in the 30° direction.
3	Draw a 20'-0" long line from A to C in the 150° direction.
4	Draw a 10'-0" long vertical line from A to D. Similarly, draw a 10'-0" long vertical line from C to E.
5	Draw a 15'-0" long vertical line from B to F.
6	Draw a 20'-0" long line in the 150° direction from F to G.
7	Draw a 20'-0" long line in the 210° direction from F to H.
8	Copy line FH to draw line GI.
9	Copy line FG to draw lines HI and DE.
10	Draw lines from D to H and E to I, and the diagram is complete.

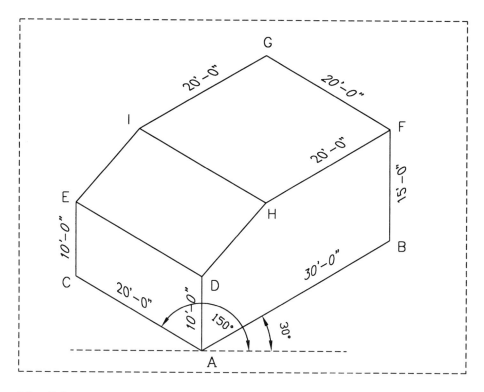

Fig. 7.3: *Drawing an isometric.*

Isometric Drawing-Aid Functions

CADD provides a number of special functions that simplify isometric drawing. The following functions are available in most CADD programs:

- Isometric grid
- Fixed cursor direction
- Isometric circles, text and dimensions
- 2D drawings to isometrics conversion

Isometric Grid

CADD allows you to draw a grid tilted 30° in both directions. The intersections of the grid can be used to draw isometric objects. You can draw a top isoplane, right isoplane or a left isoplane using these grid points. Fig. 7.4 shows an example of isometric shapes drawn using the grid points. The grid can be drawn at any specified distance as needed. When you are finished drawing an isometric, you can erase the grid.

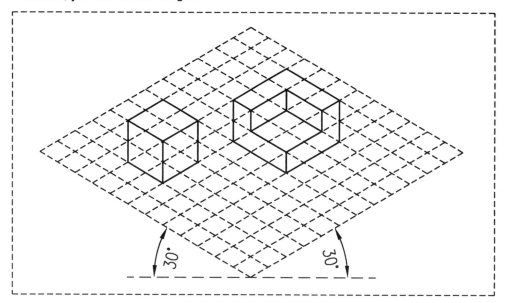

Fig. 7.4: *Drawing lines using an isometric grid.*

Fixed Cursor Direction

CADD allows you to fix the direction of the cursor at specific angles. This technique is commonly called setting the orthogonal (ortho) or constraints in many CADD programs. When the direction of the cursor is fixed, i.e., the ortho is turned on, it can move only in preset directions. This makes it easier to draw straight lines, just like using a T-square and a triangle. When working with isometrics, you can fix the direction of the cursor to multiples of 30° angles, e.g. 30°, 60°, 90°. This enables you to easily draw top isoplanes, left isoplanes and right isoplanes (See Fig. 7.5).

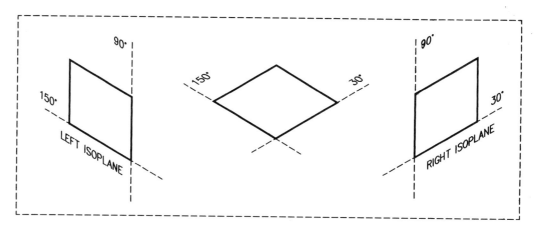

Fig. 7.5: *Fixing the direction of the cursor at isometric angles.*

Isometric Circles, Text and Dimensions

A circle appears as an ellipse when drawn in different isoplanes (See Fig. 7.6). Similarly, text and dimensions can be skewed to match the tilt of an isoplane. CADD's special isometric functions allow you to draw isometric circles, text, dimensions, symbols, etc.

To draw an isometric circle, you need to specify the radius of the circle and the isoplane to which it is to be drawn. CADD automatically draws an ellipse based on the orientation of an isoplane. Similarly, you can draw text and dimensions to match the tilt of an isoplane. This makes the text and dimensions appear to be lying parallel to a specified isoplane. Some examples of isometric text are shown in Fig. 7.6.

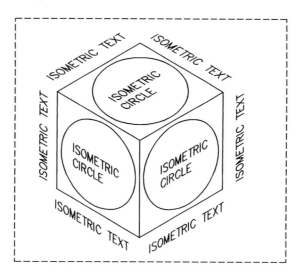

Fig. 7.6: *Drawing isometric text and circles aligned with the isoplanes.*

2D Drawings to Isometric Conversion

Special add-on programs are available that enable you to convert 2D plans and elevations into isoplanes. You can combine different isoplanes to develop an isometric. For example, you can convert a plan diagram into top isoplane and the side elevations to left and right isoplanes. CADD automatically twists all the objects of the drawing to match the tilt of the isoplane. You can place the right and left isoplanes on appropriate sides of the top isoplane. This creates a skeleton of the isometric in a few simple steps. You can finish the isometric by drawing the rest of the objects of the drawing.

Fig. 7.7 illustrates how you can draw an isometric of a building block from an existing 2D plan and elevations. Take the plan diagram and convert it into a top isoplane. This will serve as the base of the building. Convert the elevations - Side 2, Side 5 and Side 7 to right isoplanes. Move the isoplanes of the elevations on the appropriate sides of the top isoplane. This completes the basic structure of the isometric. Use this basic structure to complete the rest of the isometric.

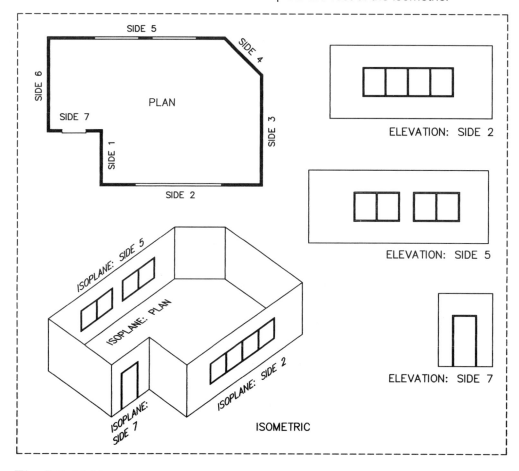

Fig. 7.7: *Making an isometric using existing 2D drawings.*

CADD PRIMER: http://www.caddprimer.com

3D Modeling

CADD's 3D modeling capabilities allow you to create 3D images that are as realistic as the actual objects. These images are called 3D models because, just like a physical model, they can be rotated on the screen. You can display views from a 3D model, such as isometrics or perspectives, from any angle with a few simple steps.

3D modeling is usually a separate CADD module that has its own set of functions. Some manufacturers market 2D programs and 3D programs as separate packages while others combine them into a single program.

The 3D models fall into the following categories:

- Wire-frame models
- Surface models
- Solid models

When you draw a model with lines and arcs, they are called wire-frame models. These models appear to be made of wires and everything in the background is visible. This does not create a very realistic effect.

Surface models are more realistic than wire-frame models. They are created by joining 3D surfaces rather than bare lines and arcs. A 3D surface is like a piece of paper that can have any dimension and can be placed at any angle to define a shape. Just like a paper model, you join surfaces to form a surface model. The views displayed from these models are quite realistic, because everything in the background can be hidden.

Solid models are considered solid inside and not hollow like a surface model. They appear to be the same as a surface model but have additional properties, such as weight, density and center of gravity, just like that of a physical object. These models are commonly used as prototypes to study engineering designs.

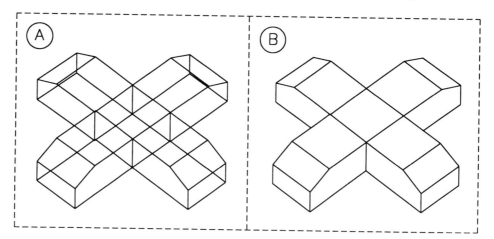

Fig. 7.8: *The concept of wire-frame model (A) and surface model (B).*

Example: You can draw a 3D model as a wire-frame, a surface model or a solid. To draw a 3D model of a cube as a wire-frame, you need to draw twelve lines by specifying 3D coordinates for each of its points. To draw it as a surface model, you need to draw all six surfaces of the cube. Although you see only three planes of the cube in front, it is essential to draw all the planes when drawing a 3D model. This ensures that a realistic view is displayed when it is rotated to display a view from any angle. When drawing a solid you can also specify its material.

Important Tip:

For general 3D drawings, wire frames and surface models are used. You start with a wire-frame model and then fill in spaces with 3D surfaces to make it more realistic.

Working with 3D Coordinates

3D coordinates are measured with the help of three axes: X, Y, and Z. The axes meet at a point in the shape of a tripod as shown in Fig. 7.9. This point is called the origin point, which is the 0,0,0 location of all coordinates. All distances can be measured using this point as a reference.

The three axes form three imaginary planes: XY plane, XZ plane and YZ plane. The XY plane is the horizontal plane and the XZ and YZ are the two vertical planes. When you need to draw something horizontal, such as the plan of a building, you draw it in the XY plane using X and Y coordinates. This generates a plan view. When you need to draw something vertical, such as an elevation of a building, you draw it using the XZ or YZ planes.

Example: To draw a line in 3D, enter two end points defined with X, Y and Z coordinates. If you need to draw the line lying flat on the ground (XY plane), the Z coordinate for both the end points of the line is zero. If you want to draw the same line at 10'-0" above the XY plane, enter the Z-coordinate for both the end points as 10'-0".

The 3D coordinates can be entered using the following formats:

- Cartesian coordinates
- Spherical coordinates
- Cylindrical coordinates

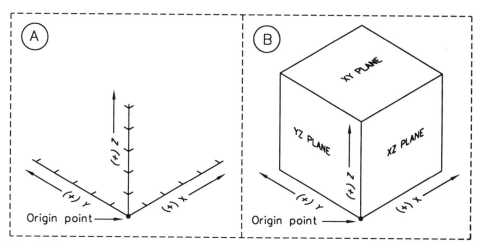

Fig. 7.9: *Measuring distances using 3D coordinates.*

Cartesian Coordinates

Cartesian coordinates are based on a rectangular system of measurement. In Chapter 2 "The CADD Basics", we discussed how Cartesian coordinates are used in 2D drawings. The same principle is applied to enter 3D coordinates with the exception that you need to enter an additional Z coordinate. Positive Z-coordinate values are used when you need to measure distances above the XY plane; negative values are used for the distances below the XY plane. The coordinates can be measured from the origin point (absolute coordinates) or from the last reference location of the cursor (relative coordinates). Coordinate values are entered separated by commas (X,Y,Z).

Fig. 7.10 illustrates the concept of the Cartesian coordinate system of measurement. Diagram A shows how the X and Y coordinates are measured in the XY plane just like 2D coordinates. Diagram B shows how to indicate height with the help of the Z coordinate. A point is located 4 units in the X direction, 6 units in the Y direction and 5.5 units in the Z direction using Cartesian coordinates.

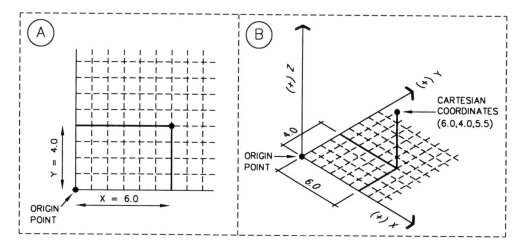

Fig. 7.10: *Measuring distances using Cartesian coordinates.*

Spherical Coordinates

Spherical coordinates are based on the longitude and latitude system of measurement (Diagram A, Fig. 7.11). Consider the origin point of the coordinate system at the center of the earth or a transparent globe. Then consider a horizontal plane (XY plane) passing through the center of the globe. To locate a point in 3D, first locate a point in the XY plane by specifying a radius and an angle (polar coordinates). To specify the height, enter an angle up or down from the XY plane (latitude).

Diagram B in Fig. 7.11 illustrates how to locate a point using spherical coordinates. The point is located in the XY plane by entering 6.0 units radius and 210° as the rotation angle (longitude). The latitude is entered as 60°.

Note:

Spherical coordinates are not very efficient for drawing purposes. They are commonly used to view a model from different angles.

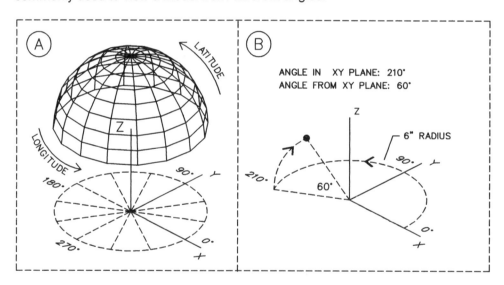

Fig. 7.11: *Measuring distances using spherical coordinates.*

Cylindrical Coordinates

Cylindrical coordinates are commonly used to draw cylindrical shapes. They are based on a cylindrical system of measurement. Consider a cylinder placed vertically and the origin point at the center of the cylinder (Fig. 7.12, Diagram A). Cylindrical coordinates are quite similar to spherical coordinates, the difference being that the Z-coordinate is specified by height and not angle.

To enter a point with the cylindrical coordinates, first you need to locate it in the XY plane just like polar coordinates. Then indicate an exact height at that point.

Diagram B in Fig. 7.12 illustrates how to locate a point using cylindrical coordinates. The point is located in the XY plane by entering 6.0 units radius arc rotated at 210°. The height is entered as 9.0 units.

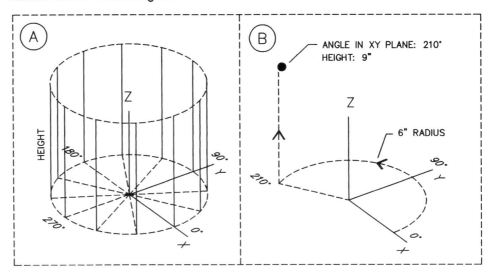

Fig. 7.12: *Measuring distances using cylindrical coordinates.*

Steps to Draw a 3D Model

The following example illustrates the basic steps to draw a 3D model of a block. The block was previously drawn as an isometric in Fig. 7.3. Now you will learn how to draw it as an actual 3D model. The same dimensions are used to draw the 3D model as were used for the isometric.

To draw the 3D model, start with the plan diagram of the block as shown in Diagram A (Fig. 7.13). When the plan diagram is complete, you can display a 3D view of the diagram that looks like Diagram B. Then you can draw vertical lines as shown in Diagram C. Finally, draw the top of the block using the end points of the vertical lines (Diagram D).

The following are the basic steps to complete the diagram shown in Fig. 7.13:

Step	Action
1	• Enter the starting point of the first line at A, which can be a point anywhere in the drawing area. • Draw a 30'-0" long horizontal line from A to B just like when drawing in 2D. You can use Cartesian coordinates to enter the values. Enter zero as the Z coordinate value for both end points. • Draw a 20'-0" long vertical line from B to C. Enter zero as the Z coordinate value for both end points. • Draw a horizontal parallel line CD at 20'-0" distance above line AB (Offset function). • Similarly, draw a vertical parallel line AD at 30'-0" distance to the left of vertical line BC. • Draw a vertical parallel line EF at 10'-0" distance to the right of line AD (Offset function). • This completes the base of the diagram. All these lines lie flat on the XY plane. The Z coordinate value for these points is zero.
2	Display a pictorial view of the diagram at a 225° angle. It displays a view as shown in Diagram B (You will learn about displaying views later in this chapter).
3	• Draw a 15'-0" long vertical line from point B to point J. Enter the Z coordinate value for point J as 15'-0". • Copy line BJ using point B as the base point and point C as the destination point. This draws the vertical line CI. • Draw a 10'-0" long vertical line from point A to point G. Enter the Z coordinate value for point G as 10'-0". • Copy line AG using point A as the base point and point D as the destination point. This draws the vertical line DH. • Move line EF 15'-0" above the XY plane. Use the move function and indicate the base point at B and relocation point at J. Note: Since the line BJ was drawn 15'-0" tall, point J is 15'-0" above point B. Using these points as a reference, automatically moves the line 15'-0" above its original location.
4	Draw lines from HK, KI, IJ, JL, LG and GH. Use the end point object snaps to pick the exact end points of lines. Note: No need to enter any 3D coordinates for these points, because the end points of the existing lines are already defined with the 3D coordinates. This completes the wire-frame model of the block as shown in Diagram D. You can convert this model into a surface model by drawing 3D surfaces for each of the planes. You can draw a surface for the top of the model by indicating the points I,J,K and L. This model requires a total of seven surfaces for all the sides: top, bottom, four sides and one inclined surface.

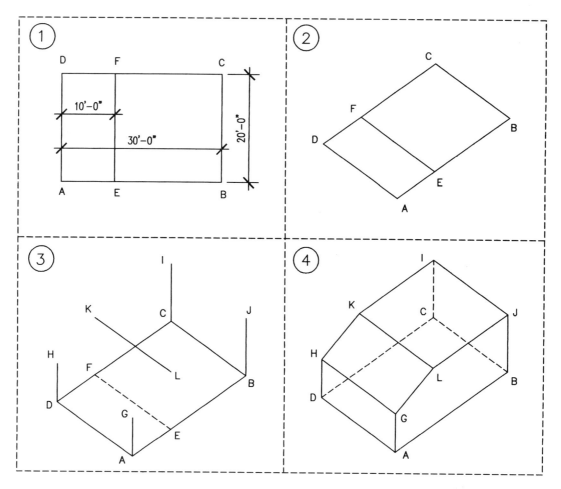

Fig. 7.13: *Drawing a 3D model.*

User-defined Coordinate System

We discussed in Chapter 2, "The CADD Basics", how a user-defined coordinate system can help to work with odd-shaped diagrams. Here is an example of using it in 3D.

Let's say you want to draw an arched object on the inclined surface of the model as shown Fig. 7.14. It is very difficult to calculate the 3D coordinates for a drawing object on the inclined surface. By creating a user-defined coordinate system, you can align the XY plane with the inclined surface of the model. Indicate the origin of the coordinate system at one corner of the inclined surface and indicate the sides of the inclined surface to be the X and Y axes (Fig. 7.14). Now the inclined surface becomes the XY plane. You can draw anything on this plane just like 2D. You don't need to worry about entering any Z coordinates. Whatever you draw will be directly drawn on this surface.

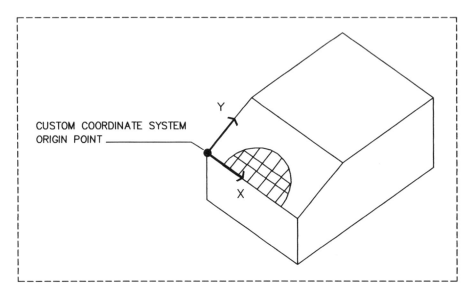

Fig. 7.14: *Drawing an arched object on the inclined surface of the model.*

Displaying Views

You can rotate a 3D model on the screen and display different views by specifying an exact viewpoint. The viewpoint represents the position of the camera from where a picture of the view is to be taken. You can define a viewpoint with the help of any of the coordinate methods discussed earlier.

There are two main protocols used to display views:

- View coordinate geometry
- Object coordinate geometry

View Coordinate Geometry

View coordinate geometry assumes that the camera (viewpoint) remains stationary and the 3D model is rotated to display a desired view. The model can be rotated around the X, Y, or Z-axis (Diagram A, Fig. 7.15). You need to specify around which axis the rotation will take place and by how much. When you rotate the model around the Z-axis, the model rotates in the XY plane; when you rotate it around the Y-axis, the rotation takes place in the XZ plane.

Object Coordinate Geometry

Object coordinate geometry assumes that the model remains stationary and the camera (viewpoint) is moved to display a desired view. You can use any of the coordinate methods to specify an exact viewpoint. Spherical coordinates are particularly helpful to indicate a viewpoint (Diagram B, Fig. 7.15).

Comparison: View coordinate geometry can be compared to holding a small model in your hand and rotating it on its sides to get a desired view. Object coordinate geometry can be compared to viewing a building from the sky. The building remains stationary, while the camera is moved to get a desired view.

Note: Most CADD programs provide both view coordinate geometry and object coordinate geometry options to display views. Depending on how you want to view a model, you can use either method.

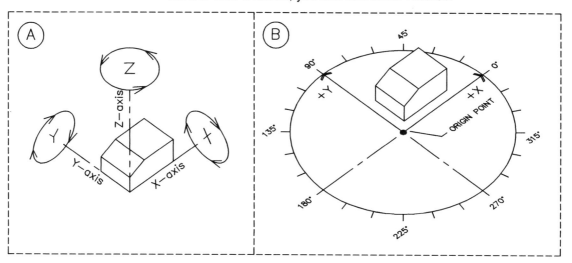

Fig. 7.15: *The concept of view coordinate geometry (A) and object coordinate geometry (B).*

Displaying Isometric Views

To display an isometric, you need to specify the direction from which the view is to be taken. The most appropriate method to indicate direction is with the help of spherical coordinates. You need to specify two angles: an angle in the XY plane (longitude) and an angle from the XY plane (latitude). The longitude determines the orientation of the model in the XY plane and the latitude determines the height of the viewpoint.

To display isometric views of the 3D model, consider the model to be lying on the XY plane (Diagram B, Fig. 7.15). The model can be viewed from four isometric positions: 45°, 135°, 225° and 315° angles.

The following chart shows the values to display the views shown in Fig. 7.16:

View	Longitude	Latitude
A	45°	35°
B	135°	35°
C	225°	35°
D	315°	35°

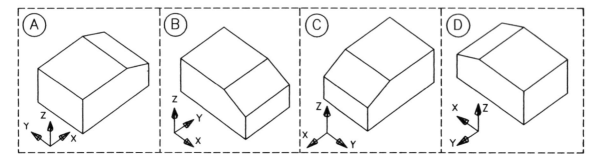

Fig. 7.16: *Displaying isometric views from different angles.*

Displaying Plans and Elevations

You can display standard 2D views such as plans and elevations by specifying the direction of the view. To display a plan view, you need to view the model from the top, that is, enter the angle from the XY plane (latitude) as 90°. To display an elevation, you need to view the model parallel to the XY plane, that is, enter the angle from the XY plane (latitude) as 0°. You can view an elevation from any angle by specifying an exact angle in the XY plane.

The following chart shows the values to display the views shown in Fig. 7.17:

View	Longitude	Latitude
A	0°	90°
B	270°	0°
C	90°	0°
D	180°	0°

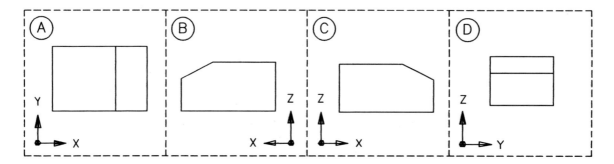

Fig. 7.17: *Displaying plans and elevations of a 3D model.*

Note:

The diagrams created in Fig. 7.16 and Fig. 7.17 show a symbol of a tripod. In most CADD programs, this symbol automatically appears when you display a 3D view. It shows the positive direction of the three axes, and acts as a guide when drawing in 3D and displaying views. The shape of the tripod is changed according to the angle of the view.

Displaying Perspective Views

CADD allows you to display perspective views from any angle of the model. You can display a true perspective by specifying an exact distance between the viewpoint and the model. (Specifying a distance is not necessary to display parallel projection views such as plans, elevations and isometrics.) When you specify an exact distance, it causes the lines of the view to converge and display a true perspective (See Fig. 7.18). The closer the viewpoint, the greater the conversion takes place.

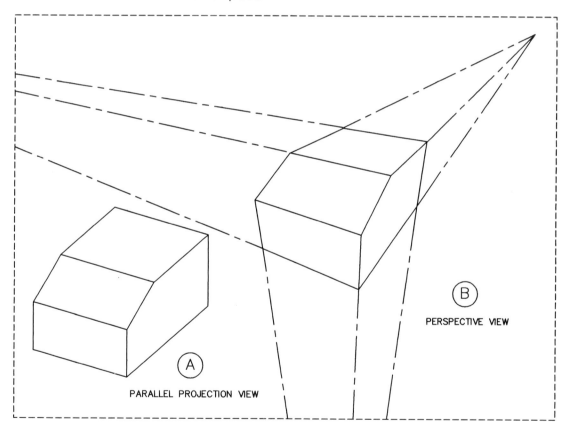

Fig. 7.18: *The concept of parallel projection views (isometrics) and perspective views.*

CADD programs use one of several methods to display perspective views. A common method is to establish a line of sight between the viewpoint (camera) and the model (target). You can specify any distance along this line of sight to display an appropriate perspective view.

Fig. 7.19 illustrates some examples of displaying perspective views of a model from different angles. Diagram A shows the plan view of the model created in Fig. 7.13 (some grid lines are added at the base of the model). The point V1 is entered as the camera position (at a certain height), and point T1 is entered as the target. This establishes a line of sight between the two points. Views B and C are displayed along this line of sight by specifying different distances. In Diagram D, a different target location is entered. This changes the direction of the line of sight. View E and F are displayed along this line of sight.

Note:

To display the model so that the lines in the background (hidden lines) are not visible, you need to convert it into a surface model. You need to draw total seven surfaces: top, bottom, four sides and one inclined surface.

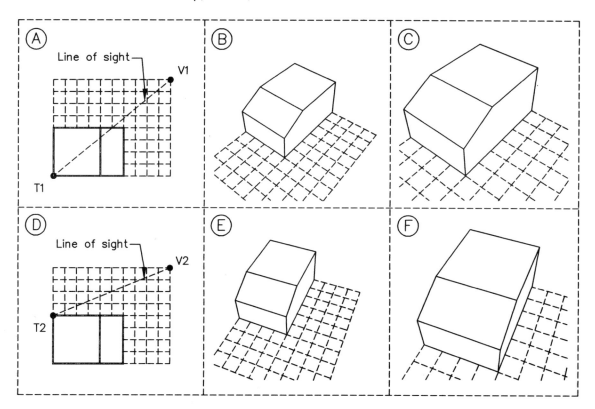

Fig. 7.19: *Displaying perspective views of a 3D model.*

Important Tips:

- You can manipulate the views of a 3D model in a number of ways. You can rotate the view, cut a section of the view along a plane, reduce or enlarge the view, change the focus of the view, hide and display certain lines, etc.

- You can display more than one view of a model on the screen at the same time. You can create a number of viewing windows (viewports) that can be used to display different views. For example, you can display a plan view of the model in one viewport, elevation in another and a perspective view in another. When you draw something in one viewport, it is automatically shown in all the viewports.

- Advanced CADD programs enable you to create animated images. You can create perspective views and store them in the computer memory. You can display a number of these images within seconds to create an animation. You can create a presentation that simulates walking through a building or the functioning of a machine.

3D Drawing-Aid Functions

The common 3D drawing-aid functions of CADD are described as follows:

- 3D ready-made shapes
- Linear extrusion
- Radial extrusion
- Shading and rendering

3D Ready-made Shapes

CADD allows you to draw a number of 3D ready-made shapes (primitives) in a few simple steps. To draw a cube, you don't need to draw all the lines or 3D faces for each of its sides. You can instantly draw a cube by specifying its dimensions. Similarly, you can draw a number of commonly used geometrical shapes just by specifying their shape and size.

Fig. 7.20 illustrates some common 3D shapes available in CADD: pyramid, prism, dome, vault, cylinder, cone, sphere, torus. To draw a pyramid, you just need to specify the number of sides and the height. To draw a sphere, specify its diameter and the number of longitudinal and latitudinal divisions (if needed). A cylinder can be drawn by indicating the height and the diameter. Similarly, you can draw other objects just by specifying their dimensions.

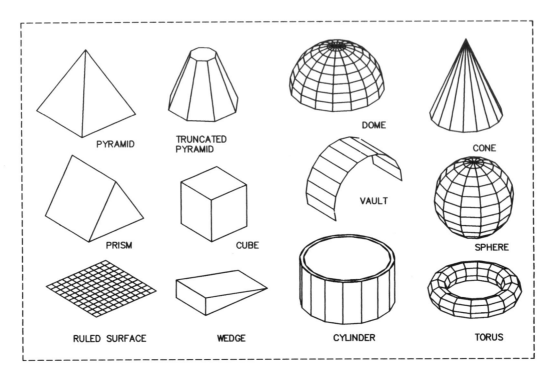

Fig. 7.20: *3D ready-made shapes available in CADD that can be instantly added to a drawing.*

Important Tip:

Specialized engineering programs provide a number of additional 3D objects and techniques to facilitate a 3D drawing. You can combine a number of 3D objects to form a single object or subtract one 3D object from another. This technique is referred to as "boolean operation". You can create a skeleton of the model using boolean operation and build the rest of the model based on it.

Extruding Objects in the Linear Direction

CADD allows you to extrude 3D shapes from 2D profiles. You can extrude a square to form a cube, a circle to form a cylinder, or a triangle to form a prism. When you use the linear extrusion function, you are prompted to select the objects to be extruded and specify the direction of extrusion (axis of extrusion). You can select any profile made of lines, arcs, polylines, or other objects and extrude it in any direction by specifying the axis of extrusion.

Fig. 7.21 illustrates how you can extrude an elevation profile of a house to make a 3D block of the house. The profile is extruded in the horizontal direction.

Fig. 7.22 illustrates how you can extrude the drawing objects in the vertical direction. In this illustration, the walls of a house as shown in the plan diagram (A) are extruded vertically to create a 3D model (B).

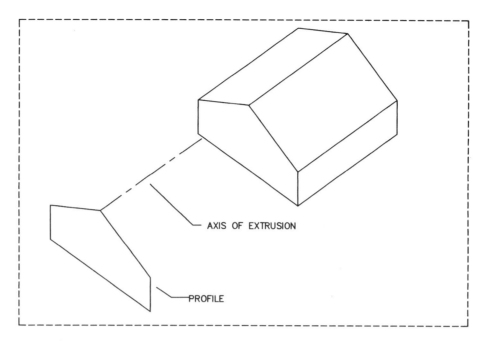

Fig. 7.21: *Drawing outline of a house from a 2D profile.*

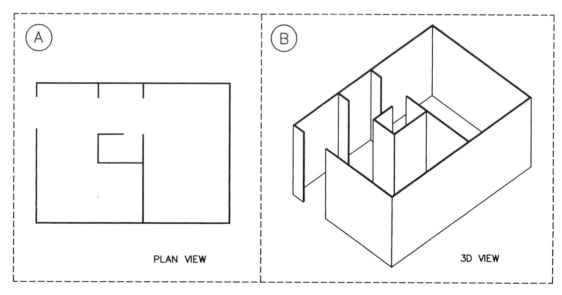

Fig. 7.22: *Drawing 3D walls from a 2D plan.*

Extruding Objects in the Circular Direction

CADD allows you to extrude drawing objects along a circular path (called radial extrusion). For example, you can draw a section of a cylinder and extrude it to form the complete cylinder. To perform a radial extrusion, you are prompted to select the objects to be extruded, indicate an axis of revolution and an angle of extrusion. The axis of revolution acts as a pivot point of the revolution and the angle of extrusion determines how much revolution will take place.

Fig. 7.23 illustrates how you can extrude a 2D profile of a flange to form a 3D model of the flange. To complete the diagram, you need to draw the section of the flange as shown in Diagram A. Indicate a vertical line as the axis of revolution. To draw only half the flange as shown in Diagram B, enter the angle of extrusion as 180°. To draw the complete flange as shown in Diagram C, enter the angle of extrusion as 360°.

Note:

CADD provides options for drawing the dividing rib lines as shown in Fig 7.22. You can specify any distance for these lines to create a 3D rendering effect.

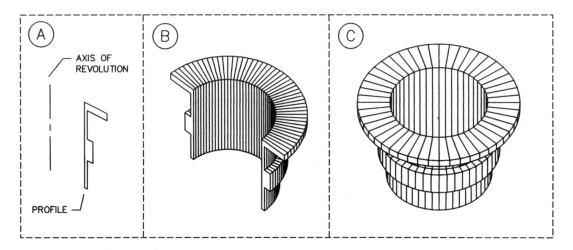

Fig. 7.23: *Drawing a 3D model of a flange from a 2D profile by extruding it in the circular direction.*

Shading and Rendering

There are a number of shading and rendering programs available that can be used to make 3D drawings very realistic. These programs allow you to create colors, shades and shadows exactly as they would appear in a picture. These programs are quite large and complex and require powerful computer hardware.

With the help of rendering programs, you can specify a number of shading and rendering parameters and create a 3D scene. You can assign colors and textures to different surfaces of a model. You can specify light sources in a scene and specify what kind of light is used and how it is directed. You can create a special setting for the model, such as a landscape or interior.

The computer analyzes all the factors specified in a scene to create a rendering. It determines how a ray of light will travel from the indicated light source to all the surfaces of the model. It determines how a surface will be lighted and where it will cast a shadow. This procedure is known as "ray tracing", and a number of rays must be traced to determine the exact lighting and shading pattern of a model.

The program determines how a color or texture will look in a certain type of light. It analyzes whether the surface is receiving direct light from the source or reflected light from other surfaces. It also takes into consideration the reflective properties of a surface. It can even calculate how the model will be reflected in glass, water or in a shining surface. It takes the computer quite some time to calculate all these factors. In some cases, the computer may need to be left uninterrupted for several minutes to generate a final image.

Important Tip:

Refer to Chapter 10 "CADD Industry Resources" for leading rendering software available in the CADD industry.

AutoCAD, MicroStation and Cadkey Terms

The following are the important terms used in leading CADD programs:
(The exact procedures vary from one program to another)

Task	AutoCAD	MicroStation	CADKEY
Entering 3D Cartesian coordinates (Absolute)	X,Y,Z	X,Y,Z	X,Y,Z
Entering 3D Cartesian coordinates (Relative)	@X,Y,Z	DX=X,Y,Z	DXV,DYV,DZV
Entering spherical coordinates	Radius<angle in XY plane<angle from XY plane	AX=Radius,angle in XY plane, angle from XY plane	Not available
Entering cylindrical coordinates	Radius<angle in XY plane, height	AX=Radius, angle in XY plane, height	Not available
Extruding objects in the linear direction	TABSURF	SURFACE OF PROJECTION	X-FORM: DELTA/ JOIN OR EXTRUDE PROFILE
Extruding objects in the circular direction	REVSURF	SURFACE OF REVOLUTION	X-FORM: ROTATE/JOIN OR X-FORM: CIRCULAR ARRAY

Example drawings created by using DataCAD: Courtesy Richard Morse, DataCAD LLC.

Printing and Plotting

Contents

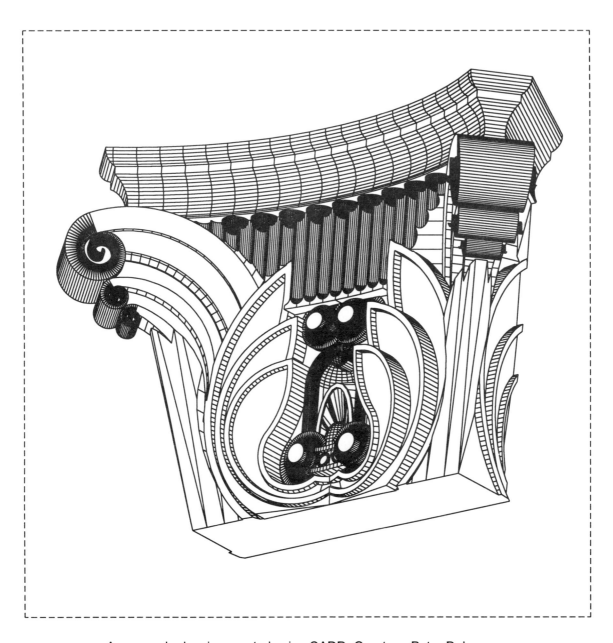

An example drawing created using CADD. Courtesy Peter Dahms.

Printing and Plotting

About this Chapter

This chapter introduces you to the printing and plotting process. It describes how the drawings are printed using a printer or a plotter. It looks at a number of issues associated with printing such as how to apply a scale to CADD drawings, how to select a sheet size and how big or small diagrams can be drawn, how to compose a drawing layout for plotting and what height text should be used based on a scale.

This chapter describes basic steps for plotting and how colors and line-weights are created in the drawings.

It also includes a discussion on common printing and plotting machines. You will learn about pen plotters, ink-jet printers/plotters, laser printers and electrostatic printers/plotters.

Key Terms in this Chapter

Term	Description
Configure	A process by which a program, such as CADD, is made to recognize and work with a hardware component, such as a plotter.
Dpi	Dots per inch; used to measure the accuracy of printing.
Line weight	Thickness of lines and other drawing objects.
Plot	To print a drawing with a plotter.
Plotting origin	An imaginary point on the screen that is used to align screen image with the paper in the plotter.
Plotting scale	To proportionally reduce or enlarge diagrams for plotting.
Plotting scale factor	A degree to which drawings are proportionally reduced or enlarged.

The Printing and Plotting Process

CADD drawings are printed using a printer or a plotter. The process of printing is as simple as selecting the print or plot function from the menu. This action sends data from the computer to a printer or plotter, which produces the final drawing. The drawings are neat, clean and, depending on the quality of the printer, highly accurate.

You can specify a number of parameters to control the size and the quality of a plot. You can plot a drawing to any size by applying an appropriate scale factor. You can specify line thickness and colors for different drawing objects. You can make a number of other adjustments as well, including rotating a plot, printing only selected areas of a drawing, or using specific fonts for text and dimensions. The following are the important considerations for plotting:

- Selecting a scale for drawings
- Composing a drawing layout
- Selecting text and dimension heights
- Choosing pens colors and line weights

Selecting a Scale for Drawings

When working on a drawing board, you use a specific scale to draw diagrams. For example, when you need to draw a plan of a building or a township, you reduce the size of the diagrams to 1/100 or 1/1000 of its actual size, that is, you use a 1:100 or 1:1000 scale. When you need to draw a small machine part, you draw it many times larger than its actual size. CADD uses the same principle to scale the drawings; however, a different approach is taken.

All CADD drawings are created on a full scale (1:1). Even if you have to draw the map of a township, you will draw it by entering the actual measurements. You can draw as big or small on the screen as you like and adjust the image using view-display functions. The magnification of the image has no relevance to the actual scale of the drawing. The actual scale of the drawing is determined when the drawings are plotted. If you drew a 36'-0" x 24'-0" rectangle and you want to fit it on a 36" x 24" paper, you need to scale it down to 1/12th, that is, you need to apply 1" = 1'-0" scale.

The dimensions you enter on-screen are called "drawing units" (or master units); the actual size that is printed on paper is measured with "plotter units". When you enter the plot function, the plot dialog box opens to allow you to specify the ratio between drawing units and plotter units. The ratio between the plotting units and drawing units is called "scale factor". The scale factor determines how big or small the drawing will be printed. The following table shows some of the common scales used in architectural and engineering drawings and the scale factors associated with them:

Common scales in feet-inch format		Scale factor
1" = 1"	(full size)	1
1" = 1'-0"	(reduced 12 times)	12
1/2" = 1'-0"	(reduced 24 times)	24
1/4" = 1'-0"	(reduced 48 times)	48
1/8" = 1'-0"	(reduced 96 times)	96

Common scales in metric format		Scale factor
1:1	(full size)	1
1:10	(reduced 10 times)	10
1:20	(reduced 20 times)	20
1:50	(reduced 50 times)	50
1:100	(reduced 100 times)	100

When starting a drawing, one of the first steps is to determine the plotting scale and sheet size. This is calculated the same way as it is when working on a drawing board. You choose a scale and a sheet size based on the size of the diagrams. You can calculate the maximum size diagram that can fit on a sheet by multiplying the scale factor with the sheet size.

Once the plotting scale and sheet size are determined, you can draw a border on-screen representing the maximum drawing area. The border reminds you that this is the maximum size diagram you can draw on that size sheet. All drawing objects must be contained within this border; otherwise they will fall outside the plotting area.

Composing a Drawing Layout

CADD provides a number of special functions to compose a drawing layout. You can arrange diagrams on a sheet as you like and apply any scale factor. Different programs use different protocols to accomplish this task.

A common protocol used in AutoCAD and many other popular programs is as follows: To compose a drawing layout, you can activate a special mode of working called paper space or plot layout. The paper space represents the actual sheet size. You can arrange any number of diagrams on this sheet and apply a scale factor to diagrams individually. It shows exactly how the diagram will be plotted on the selected sheet size.

Another protocol used involves specifying the plotting scale and sheet size when you start a drawing. You enter all the drawing measurements in actual size and the computer automatically draws them to a selected scale. If you draw a 100'-0"x100'-0" square using a 1:100 scale, it will automatically scale it down and you can see exactly how it is going to fit on the sheet.

Regardless of which method is used for composing the drawing, you can create a border and title block that you would like to use for a project and store that drawing file in the CADD library. You can use this title block for all your drawings in the project for a consistent look.

The following table shows some of the standard sheet sizes (in inches):

ANSI		ISO		Architectural	
Mark	**Size**	**Mark**	**Size**	**Mark**	**Size**
A	8.5x11	A4	8.3x11.7	A	9x12
B	11x17	A3	11.7x16.5	B	12x18
C	17x22	A2	16.5x23.4	C	18x24
D	22x34	A1	23.4x33.1	D	24x36
E	34x44	A0	33.1x46.8	E	36x48

Important Tip:

US National CAD standards have established guidelines for sheet organization and the design of title blocks. Fig. 8.1 shows an example of a drawing created using these guidelines. The drawing area of the sheet is divided into columns and rows. Each column is identified with a number and each row is identified with a letter. This grid system helps to arrange the diagrams and to identify them using this grid system. A title block is located on the right side of the drawing. It contains blocks of information associated with the drawing and the project. National CAD Standards also include guideline to organize information within the title block. For more information about US National CAD standards, visit their web site at http://www.nationalcadstandard.org.

Selecting Text and Dimension Heights

As diagrams are enlarged or reduced by applying a scale factor, the size of text, dimensions, patterns and symbols is also changed. When you place different scale diagrams on the same sheet, you may get different sized text for each diagram. This is generally not acceptable for professional drawings. It is better to have consistently sized text on the drawings regardless of their scale.

To achieve a standard text height for all the diagrams, you need to write text according to the scale of the diagrams. Let's say you want to print 1" high text for your final plots. If you like to use 1:50 scale for a diagram, you need to enter text 50 times larger than the printed size (50" high). When 1:50 scale factor is applied, it reduces the entire diagram (including text) by 1/50th. This results in 1" high printed text.

You can choose text heights that you would like to use in a project and prepare a table that shows the heights based on the scale of diagrams. Let's say you want the printed text height to be 1/8". You can calculate the text height for different scale diagrams using the following calculation:

Text height to enter on-screen = (Printed text height x scale factor).

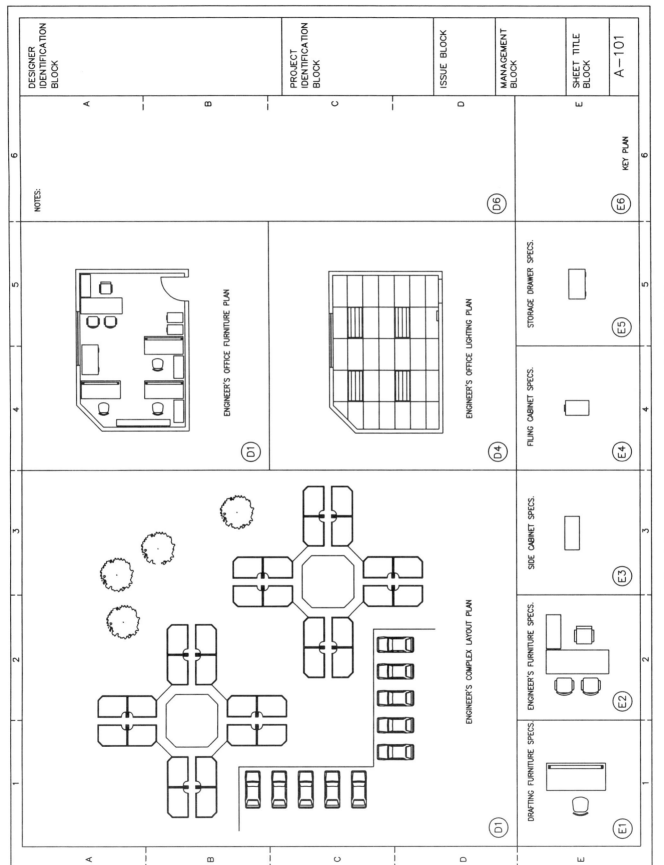

Fig. 8.1: An example drawing created using CADD.

The following table shows some examples of calculating the text height:

Printed text height	Plotting scale	Scale factor	Text height to enter on-screen
1/8"	1:1	1	1/8"
1/8"	1/2" = 1'-0"	24	3"
1/8"	1/4" = 1'-0"	48	6"
1/8"	1/8" = 1'-0"	96	12"

Note:

There are hundreds of fonts available that you can use with CADD. The fonts used in the drawing must be compatible with the printer or plotter used for plotting.

Choosing Pens, Colors and Line weights

CADD allows you to work with a variety of colors and line weights depending upon the plotter. In most CADD programs, the colors you use on-screen are configured with a specific line weight in the plotter. For example, the objects drawn with red color on-screen may be printed with .5mm line weight; the objects drawn with blue color may be printed with .2mm line weight. These are called pen assignments. You can choose any pen assignments for plotting.

Note: In most CADD programs line weights are not displayed on-screen, but the drawing is printed according to the line weights. Advanced programs include special functions, allowing you to view the line weights on-screen as well.

When setting up a plotter, one of the first steps is to configure line weights and colors available in the plotter with the CADD program. This means assigning each line weight in the plotter with a color or pen number in the drawing. You may want to make a table showing all the line weights and colors a plotter can produce and match them with the pen assignments you would like to use.

Most companies use their own pen assignments for plotting. If one company sends a drawing to other companies, it may not print the same way, because other companies may have their own pen assignments. US National CADD Standard has taken the initiative to solve this problem. They have established standards for pen assignments as described below:

Standard pen assignments established by US National CADD Standard:

On-screen color	AutoCAD Pen #	MicroStation pen #	line weight
Red	1	3	0.007"
Yellow	2	4	0.010"
Green	3	2	0.014"
Cyan	4	7	0.014"
Blue	5	1	0.020"
Magenta	6	5	0.039"
White/black	7	0	0.055"

Steps to Plotting

The following are the basic steps to plotting.
(The exact procedures vary from one program to another.)

Step	Action
1	Set up the plotter according to the manufacturer's specifications and configure it with your CADD program.
2	Place paper in the plotter and run a self test to ensure that the paper path is clear and the pens or cartridges are in good working condition.
3	Display the drawing to be plotted on the screen and choose the Plot function.
4	Respond to the specific prompts of your CADD program. In general, a CADD program will require the following information to plot the drawing: **Plotting area:** You can plot a part of the drawing or the entire drawing. You will be able to indicate the plotting area by indicating a window (an imaginary rectangle formed by two diagonal points) or by selecting a specific view for plotting. **Plotting scale factor:** Enter a scale factor based on how big or small you want to print the drawing and the sheet size used. (See topic "Selecting a Scale for Drawings.") **Plotting origin:** The plotting origin is a point that allows you to align the drawing shown on the screen with the paper in the plotter (see Fig. 8.2). You can place the diagrams on the paper anywhere by entering the exact coordinates of the plotting origin.

Important Tip:

It's always better to do a test plot of a small area of the drawing before sending all the drawings to plotter or printer.

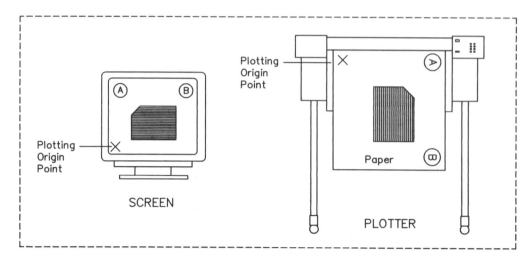

Fig. 8.2: *Aligning the screen image with the paper in the plotter.*

Printers and Plotters

Printers and plotters are used to print CADD drawings. The drawings are generally printed at about 300-600 dpi (dots per inch) accuracy, which is considered quite high precision for engineering drawings. There are machines available that can print at 1200 dpi or higher accuracy as well.

The following are some examples of printers and plotters:

- Pen plotters
- Ink-jet printers/plotters
- Laser printers
- Electrostatic printers/plotters

Pen Plotters

Pen plotters create drawings by plotting vectors. They create a drawing by moving pens on the media (the paper) or by simultaneously moving the media as well as the pens. Normal drafting pens are fitted into the mechanical arm of the plotter, which moves to draw the objects. These pens are set in an adapter that has numbered slots. You can place different thickness or color pens in to slots based on the pen assignments set in the CADD application.

There are two kinds of pen plotters: flatbed plotters and drum plotters. They essentially do the same task but work on different principles. With flatbed plotters, the paper is fixed on a flat panel, and a mechanical arm with pens moves over it to create the drawing. With drum plotters, both the paper and the pens move to create drawings. The paper moves over a drum vertically and the mechanical arm holding the pens moves horizontally, simultaneously.

Note: The pen plotters used to be very common. With the advancements in the technology, other printing machines have become available and pen plotters are rarely used.

Ink-Jet Printers/Plotters

Ink-jet printers/plotters use ink cartridges for drawing rather than pens. The flow of ink is monitored with electrodes that inject ink through very fine channels in the cartridge. It creates line thickness. Color cartridges are available to produce color drawings. These devices used to be messy because the ink would often leak from the cartridge. However, significant improvements have been made and now they are considered maintenance free. Ink-jet printers plotters are affordable and are most commonly used.

Laser Printers

Laser printers work on the principles of electrography, which are commonly applied in copier machines. These devices use a photo conductor drum that is coated with photosensitive material. The screen image is transferred to the drum with a laser scan. The image from the drum is transferred to a printing medium, leaving an electronic charge on it. The printing medium is then passed through a toner applicator that is charged opposite. The carbon particles of the toner stick to the printing media to produce the final drawing. It takes only a few seconds to complete the entire process. Laser printers print from 300 dpi to 1200 dpi and commonly use 8 1/2" by 11" or 11" by 17" paper.

Electrostatic Printers/Plotters

Electrostatic printers/plotters use a number of charging heads to create an electronic image on the plotting medium. The charging heads are positioned along the entire length of the plotter. As the paper moves, these heads move up or down leaving a positive or negative charge. This creates an electronic image on the paper. The paper is then passed through a toner applicator to produce a final drawing the same way as laser printers.

Electrostatic plotters are available to print large sheets at 300 dpi to 1200 dpi accuracy. A device with 600 dpi accuracy has 600 heads within a 1-inch length of the paper. If the plotter covers 36 inch-wide paper, it has (600x36) 21,600 writing heads. Electrostatic plotters take just about 30 seconds to plot a drawing that could take 30 minutes with a pen plotter. These machines are expensive.

Fig. 8.3: *An electrostatic plotter by OCE Technologies intended for commercial use. Photo courtesy OCE Technologies, The Netherlands. http://www.oce.nl*

AutoCAD, MicroStation and Cadkey Terms

The following are the important terms used in leading CADD programs: (The exact procedures vary from one program to another)

Task	AutoCAD	MicroStation	CADKEY
Plotting a drawing	PLOT	PRINT/PLOT	PRINT/PLOT
Drawing creation mode	MODEL SPACE	N/A	MODEL
Drawing composition mode	PAPER SPACE	PLOT LAYOUT	LAYOUT MODE
Selecting an area for plotting	PLOT: WINDOW, VIEW	PLOT: FENCE, VIEW	PRINT/PLOT (specify region)
Applying scale to drawings	PLOTTED UNITS: DRAWING UNITS	MASTER UNITS: PLOTTER UNITS	PRINT/PLOT (specify scale)

Maximizing CADD

Contents

An example drawing created using CADD. Courtesy Eaglepoint software.

Maximizing CADD

About this Chapter

So far, we have concentrated on CADD's drawing capabilities. But CADD is able to do much more than just drawing. It can help you design, perform analyses, and accomplish many automated tasks. There are a number of applications for CADD in architectural design, engineering calculations, product design, etc.

This chapter contains two main topics:

- *Streamlining CADD Drawing Environment*
- *The Design Applications of CADD*

Streamlining CADD Drawing Environment describes how to maximize CADD's drawing efficiency using symbol libraries, macros and customizing features. It also describes how CADD can be used to prepare project reports and cost estimates using database functions.

The Design Application of CADD describes how CADD can help you in design work. It outlines some categories of artificial intelligence programs associated with CADD and describes the concepts behind them.

Note: The objective of this topic is to give an overview of research and development taking place in the field of CADD. It introduces you to some of techniques and terms used in the artificial intelligence (AI) CADD industry. Although, artificial intelligence is out of the scope of this book, the resources listed here can give a glimpse of the AI CADD industry.

Key Terms in this Chapter

Term	Description
Artificial intelligence (AI)	A computer capability that enables the computer to think and make decisions.
Attribute	A description of a drawing object that is directly linked with the drawing.
CAFM	An acronym for Computer Aided Facility Management.
Database	A collection of data that can be extracted in several formats.
Design automation	A term associated with making the design procedures automatic.
Download	A procedure for transferring electronic files from a web site to a remote computer.
Drawing automation	A term associated with making the drawing process automatic.
DWF	
FEM	An acronym for Finite Element Method. It is programming technique commonly used for structural design programs.
FTP	An acronym for File Transfer Protocol. It is a procedure used to upload and download files on the Internet.
Fuzzy-logic	A programming technique used in artificial intelligence programs that can draw conclusions even if the statements are not completely true or false.
Integrated system	A group of programs that can work together as one package.
Intelligent CAD	A computer program with artificial intelligence and CADD capabilities.
Knowledge-based system	A category of artificial intelligence programs that makes use of information gathered from previous projects.
Lisp	A programming language used in AutoCAD.
Macro	A set of commands recorded in a file and played back to perform a task.
Parametric modeling	A capability of CADD that links calculations with the geometry of diagrams.
Spreadsheet	An electronic chart that contains information in rows and columns.
SVF	
Upload	A procedure for transferring electronic files to a web site from a remote computer.

Streamlining CADD Drawing Environment

When you start working with a new CADD program, it can be very slow to work with in the beginning. You can get efficient with CADD only when you use shortcut methods and special editing techniques, develop symbol libraries and implement prototype drawing standards.

The following are some of the essentials for maximizing CADD:

- Developing CADD symbol libraries
- Using macros
- Add-on CADD software
- Customizing CADD
- Using CADD database

Developing CADD Symbol Libraries

There are many symbols used in drawings that you may need to draw again and again. You don't need to draw these symbols every time you need them. You can draw them once and store them in special directories. These directories act as symbol libraries that can be readily accessed whenever you need a symbol.

Commonly used symbol libraries are available through CADD vendors. These libraries include standard furniture, doors and window symbols, electrical and mechanical symbols, landscape symbols, presentation symbols, graphic signs, etc. Fig. 9.1 illustrates an example of an electrical symbol library commonly used by electrical engineers. You can instantly add any of the symbols to a drawing just by selecting them from the symbol library.

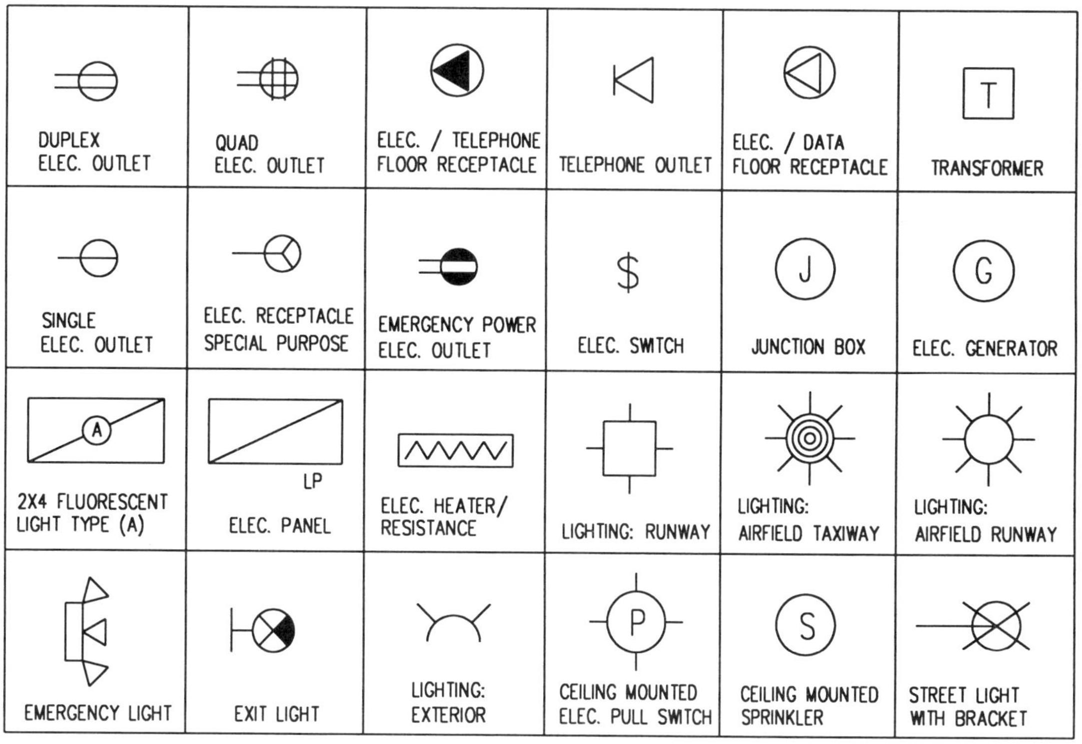

DUPLEX ELEC. OUTLET	QUAD ELEC. OUTLET	ELEC. / TELEPHONE FLOOR RECEPTACLE	TELEPHONE OUTLET	ELEC. / DATA FLOOR RECEPTACLE	TRANSFORMER
SINGLE ELEC. OUTLET	ELEC. RECEPTACLE SPECIAL PURPOSE	EMERGENCY POWER ELEC. OUTLET	ELEC. SWITCH	JUNCTION BOX	ELEC. GENERATOR
2X4 FLUORESCENT LIGHT TYPE (A)	ELEC. PANEL	ELEC. HEATER/ RESISTANCE	LIGHTING: RUNWAY	LIGHTING: AIRFIELD TAXIWAY	LIGHTING: AIRFIELD RUNWAY
EMERGENCY LIGHT	EXIT LIGHT	LIGHTING: EXTERIOR	CEILING MOUNTED ELEC. PULL SWITCH	CEILING MOUNTED SPRINKLER	STREET LIGHT WITH BRACKET

Fig 9.1: *An example of an electrical symbol library.*

Note:

US National CADD standard committee has developed a number of symbol libraries for different engineering disciplines. More information about these symbol libraries can be obtained by visiting their web site at http://www.nationalcadstandard.org.

Using Macros

A macro is a set of instructions recorded in a file that can be played back to perform a task. A sequence of instructions can be stored as a macro, which can be run at any time. As a result, using a macro can reduce a complex and lengthy process down to a single click of a mouse button or key.

Many CADD programs provide include built-in capabilities to use macros. In these programs, writing a macro is as simple as selecting the "record macro" and "play macro" functions. When the record macro function is selected, whatever sequence of commands you enter are recorded in the macro. You can name the macro as you like and play it back when required. In other programs you need to manually write the commands in a separate file that can be run as a macro.

A macro can be written to accomplish almost any CADD task. For example, you can write a macro to display a series of views to make a presentation on the screen. Or you can write a macro to make the same corrections to a number of drawings. Whenever you find yourself repeating a task, using a macro is a perfect solution.

Note:

A common problem encountered with macros is that they get stuck when they encounter an unexpected condition in a drawing or when they need certain data input not specified in the macro. It requires thorough checking and testing to make them workable; but it is worth the effort if the task is to be repeated often.

CADD Drawing Automation

It is the dream of a CADD user to have CADD do as much work as possible. Can CADD be used to draw elevations from plans? Can it dimension the drawing automatically? Can it draw a 3D view from plans and elevations? With the help of advanced programming, it is possible to accomplish all of these tasks.

Many software developers have started to focus on the drawing automation aspect of CADD. There are a number of discipline specific (or add-on programs) available, that can help automate drawing work. For example, an architectural CADD program includes a number of features to automatically draw doors, windows, staircases, bathrooms, kitchens, ceiling grids, floor tiles patterns, etc.

To draw a draw a staircase, you don't need to do all the calculations and draw every component of the staircase line by line. You just need to indicate the floor-to-floor height, the width of the staircase, and choose from a number of staircase styles available. CADD automatically calculates how many steps will be required and draws them automatically. It can draw plans, sections, elevations and 3D view of the staircase. If you need to change the floor-to-floor height or the style of the staircase, the drawing can be updated in a few simple steps.

Customizing CADD

Customizing CADD plays a major role in achieving drawing efficiency. Most CADD programs allow you to customize them to some extent. You can accomplish the following by customizing CADD:

- You can arrange menus on the screen, as you like. You place your most commonly used functions in such a way that they are easily accessed, and get rid of the functions that you rarely use.

- You can develop keyboard shortcuts to enter commands, such as "L" for line or "A" for arc.

- You can set up the working environment of CADD as per your requirements. You can set up standard sheet sizes, text styles, dimension styles, layers, line styles, pen numbers, fonts, etc., and instantly apply them to a drawing.

- With some knowledge of programming, you may be able customize the commands to work as per your specific needs. You may be able to add new functions to accomplish specific tasks.

- There are hundreds of add-on features available from independent third-party vendors that may facilitate your work. These third-party add-ons can make the drawing work much simpler.

Using CADD Database

CADD allows you to develop a database that is linked with the diagrams in the drawing. You can add descriptions of drawing objects (attributes) in the database and link them to diagrams. The attributes can be used to describe many characteristics of diagrams, such as size, color, area and price. If you draw a symbol of a chair, it is just lines and arcs in computer memory; the computer does not know what it is. With the help of special CADD functions, you can describe all the attributes associated with it.

The computer can link hundreds of attributes to a symbol and keep all the records in a database. The data stored in the form of a database has an advantage that it can be outputted in different formats. The database can be used to prepare reports and to perform analyses. These capabilities are particularly helpful in managing large projects.

The report generated using the database function of CADD is quite different from preparing such a report manually using non-intelligent CADD functions. If you calculate the area of a rectangle and write the area next to it using the text command, it becomes just text in the computer memory. It has no meaning to the computer. When the area is calculated using the database functions, it is directly linked with the drawing. The computer recognizes the attribute as the area of the rectangle and keeps a record of it. If a change is made to the diagram and the area is changed, it is automatically updated in the spreadsheet. It also updates all the values associated with the area in the spreadsheet.

Important Tip:

There are a number of add-on programs available that specialize in database capabilities. There is a specific category of software just for facility management called computer-aided facility management (CAFM) software. These programs are designed to keep records of furniture, equipment, areas, linear units, etc., associated with buildings. Popular CAFM programs include: Archibus, Drawbase and Aperture. (See Chapter 10 for contact information.)

The Design Applications of CADD

Although CAD is an acronym for computer-aided design and CADD for computer-aided design and drafting most programs do not offer any design capabilities. They are just drafting programs, but manufacturers call them CAD or CADD anyway. You may be able to work out designs using the drafting capabilities of CADD, but that is not real computer-aided design. A CADD program can be truly called a design program only when it has the ability to solve problems and perform analyses.

Design is a vast subject and has different applications for different professionals. It has a specific meaning to an architect, a structural engineer, a civil engineer or a mechanical engineer. An architect may use CADD to design a building part, a structural engineer may use it for a design calculation and a civil engineer may use it for certain site design analysis.

The design applications of CADD are still a subject of research. Many academic institutes offer postgraduate courses dedicated to research and development of CADD design software. Some design programs have been developed for engineering applications, but generally they need to be customized.

Design programs are based on a number of principles and vary significantly in their approach. Some are mainly based on calculations, some involve comparison and logic in the program, while others involve the use of a database or another form of artificial intelligence. The following are some examples of design programs:

- Calculation programs
- Intelligent CAD
- Knowledge-based CAD systems

Calculation Programs

Calculation programs are extremely effective in solving complex mathematical problems. Specialized engineering CADD programs are designed to compute scientific, trigonometric, logarithmic and exponential functions. They can be used to perform many inter-connected calculations. If one variable in the calculation is changed, the program automatically adjusts the rest of the calculations. For example, a structural engineer working with frame structures does not have to calculate all the members each time a new span or load is added to the structure. The computer program understands that everything else is constant except the load and the span and can give the end results within seconds.

A useful advancement in calculation programs is parametric modeling. Parametric modeling enables the user to link calculations with the geometric drawing. Certain graphic elements and dimensions are linked with the end results of the calculations. The computer automatically adjusts the geometry based on the calculations, or it can be programmed to adjust the calculations based on the geometry. Parametric modeling is commonly used to create computer-generated simulations of machine parts.

References:

- Structural design engineering software: http://www.xfemily.com/index.htm

- Simulation video gallery: http://caad.arch.ethz.ch/main.html

- CAD program for the analysis and design of electromagnetic and thermal devices: http://www.magsoft-flux.com/

Intelligent CAD

Intelligent CAD programs are based on logic and comparison, and have a number of applications in product design, mechanical design, space planning, etc. These programs are not based purely on mathematics as the calculation programs. Besides mathematics, they analyze forms, shapes, arrangement of objects, patterns, colors, etc. They can draw conclusions even if the resulting statements are not completely true or false (a technique known as Fuzzy-logic).

Intelligent CAD programs make decisions based on hundreds of parameters defined in the program. For example, a road design program can help in developing road layouts based on the road-construction criteria. It can analyze whether a particular road design is appropriate to hand a given traffic. It can analyze the width of the road, turning radius, code violations and other constructibilty issues based on the traffic patterns.

Another example of an intelligent CAD program is space planning. A designer can use a design program to make furniture layouts. The program is designed to control parameters associated with the layout, such as minimum and maximum distance between tables and acceptable orientation of chairs and tables. The program can address hundreds of specified do's and don'ts and prepare design alternatives.

References:

- Automatic review tool for CAD/CAM drawings (road design):
  http://www.shai.com/projects/auto_review.htm

- Artificial Intelligence in AutoCAD with Lisp (furniture layout):
  http://xarch.tu-graz.ac.at/autocad/adge/CAMP_Adge96_AI.html

Knowledge-based CAD Systems

Knowledge-based CAD systems (also known as expert systems), make use of information gathered from previous projects (or parameters defined by the programmer) and use it for new design proposals. The knowledge-based systems enable large corporations to constantly improve their design and manufacturing process. Let's say an engineering firm specializes in automobile design. They may have designed dozens of automobiles and have encountered hundreds of design problems associated with them. To design a new automobile, they don't need to address all the issues again. They can use the information gathered in the knowledge-based system to find quick solutions.

Knowledge-based systems are capable of addressing thousands of rules defined in the program. They make decisions based on these predefined rules. This process is referred to as rule-based reasoning. An advanced form of this process is called case-based reasoning that allows the user to define a new set of rules case by case.

References:

- Knowledge Technologies International offers a number of knowledge-based solutions for large corporations such as British Aerospace, Boeing, Jaguar and BMW: http://www.ktiworld.com

- CAD Research Center, Polytechnic State University, California has developed a knowledge-based system called ICADS. In contains building design information that can be used by architects to address environmental concerns in buildings: http://www.csc.calpoly.edu/~cadrc/

Integrated Systems

Integrated systems are a group of systems and software that can work in a network environment and share information. This approach is commonly adopted in large corporations that need hundreds of computers networked. The integrated systems are designed to include different application programs in one package. The programs are able to work as independent programs as well as share information.

Example: A large manufacturing company having multiple departments can use an integrated system to accomplish many tasks. An integrated system can include CADD software for the engineering department, manufacturing software for the manufacturing department, accounting software for the accounting department, and so on.

The significance of an integrated system is that it enables one department to use relevant information produced by other departments. For example, different departments can use the CADD drawing to accomplish their tasks. A manufacturing program can use the drawing to set its machines according to the drawing coordinates. The accounting department can use CADD spreadsheets to prepare estimates. A sales manager can monitor the progress of the project by accessing status reports for each department.

Large corporations often have customized integrated software packages that can meet their exact needs. They can include all the capabilities from design to drafting to database management. Integrated systems contribute to a highly productive environment. There are a number of such packages available in the CADD industry today. CADDS, CATIA-CADAM, MEDUSA, MICROCADAM, PRO/ENGINEER are some of the examples. (See Chapter 10 for contact information.)

Collaborating CADD Projects on the Internet

Internet is changing the way professionals collaborate CADD projects. Professionals can work as team and share CADD drawings with others thousands of miles away. The drawings can be sent using the E-mail and are delivered within minutes. Another method of distributing drawings is FTP. Using the FTP method, you can upload the CADD drawing files to specific server or web site. Any one with access to that server or web site can download the drawings. The E-mail and FTP methods are ideal for distributing drawings, however they do not provide real-time interaction between the team members.

There are a number of project collaboration software available that allow you to instantly publish your drawings on the web. Most CADD programs include tools that allow you to export the drawings to a format that can be instantly published on the web. Two common formats available are DWF and SVF. The drawings in these formats can be viewed on the web by using a browser that has special plug-in to display these formats.

Advanced project collaboration software allows you to mark CADD drawings and share it with others in real-time. You can have a virtual meeting with your team members who may be located in different cities. You can create and edit drawings right in front of them and they can provide their feedback right away.

There is a lot of development taking place with respect to CADD technology on the web. Some of the CADD software companies offer the use of CADD and collaboration software right from their web site. You don't need to buy and install the software on your computer. You can rent it and use it directly from their web site.

The following are some of the important project collaboration resources on the Internet.

Description	Internet address
AutoCAD iX (Internet extension) tools allow you to view and mark up CAD drawings and have a virtual meeting on the web	http://www.avat.com
Bentley Systems Model Server: A server software that allows you exchange drawings in a number of formats	http://msdiscovery.bentley.com
Dr. DWG Internet Drawing Collaborator: A server software allows to exchange 3D models in different formats	http://www.drdwg.com
Alibre Design from Alibre, Inc.: Web-based design software for mechanical design and solid modeling, viewing and markup	http://www.alibre.com
OneSpace from CoCoreate: Includes a number of real-time CAD product development tools	http://www.cocreate.com
Constuctw@re Internet plan room from Construct@re: A project collaboration software for architect and construction firms to coordinate construction process	http://www.constructware.com

CADD Artificial Intelligence (AI) Resources

Description	Internet address
Special interest group on design automation (SIGDA) home page	http://jamaica.ee.pitt.edu/
People in CAD (University of California)	http://www-cad.eecs.berkeley.edu/
A CAD thesis project by Mr. Otto Salomons, University of Twente, The Netherlands	http://www.pt.wb.utwente.nl/staff/otto/thesis/chapter1.html
An archive of hundreds of research papers on computer aided design	http://itc.fgg.uni-lj.si/cumincad/
Architecture and CAAD research: Swiss Federal Institute of Technology, Zurich	http://caad.arch.ethz.ch/main.html
University of Sydney's Key Center of Design Computing and Cognition	http://www.arch.su.edu.au/kcdc/
CAD design research paper: Prof. Robin Drogemuller and Prof. John D. Smith, Australia	http://www.jcu.edu.au/~csrd/Publications/PAP_95/PAP_95.html
CAD Research Center, California Polytechnic State University	http://www.cadrc.calpoly.edu/
Leading developer of intelligent CAD software using artificial intelligence. The web site includes comprehensive AI links.	http://www.shai.com/

Description	Internet address
Knowledge Technologies International: Knowledge-based solutions for manufacturing	http://www.ktiworld.com/home.shtml
CAD research paper: Prof. Ziga Turk, University of Ljubljana, Slovenia.	http://fgg.uni-lj.si/~zturk/drafts/ascona.98/
The University of Edinburgh, Scotland: Postgraduate courses offered on architectural design and computing	http://www.caad.ed.ac.uk/
People in USC CAD group (University of Southern California)	http://atrak.usc.edu/people.html
CAD Center: A postgraduate teaching & research unit – Scotland.	http://www.cad.strath.ac.uk/

Important Tips:

- The following are some of the keywords associated with the CADD research and development industry. They can be entered in a search engine on the Internet to find relevant information.

  AI CAD, INTELLEGENT CAD, CAD FUZZY LOGIC, KNOWLEDGE-BASED CAD, CASE-BASED CAD, CAD FEM, DRAWING AUTOMATION, DESIGN AUTOMATION, POSTGRADUATE CAD RESEARCH

- CADD programs are constantly being updated. There are new features added every time a new release comes out. However, the future of the CADD industry lies in the drawing automation and artificial intelligence programs. The advancement in this field has just begun. There are only a few such programs currently available; it is a wide-open field for anyone to explore. We will certainly see more advancement in this field over the next decade.

An example drawing created using CADD.

CADD Industry Resources

10

About this Chapter

Implementing CADD is a big expense. It is worth the extra effort to take the time you need to select the right CADD program. With so many programs available, it is likely to get confusing. Each CADD vendor claims his or her product to be superior. The best answer may come if you review each program in light of your requirements.

This chapter describes the general criteria for selecting a CADD program and lists a number of leading CADD products and resources. Note that most companies offer more than one CADD program and may be able to customize the program with add-on programs.

Note: You can access all the resources listed here through a web site dedicated to this book at http://www.caddprimer.com.

CADD Industry Terms

Term	Description
AEC	Architecture, engineering and construction application.
ANSI	American National Standards Institute
Boolean modeling	A 3D modeling technique that allows to add or subtract 3D shapes from one model to another.
CAE	Computer aided engineering.
CAFM	Computer aided facility management
CAM	Computer aided manufacturing
CGM	Computer graphics metafile
DXF	Data exchange format - A standard format commonly used to exchange drawings from one application to another
EDM	Engineering document management
GIS	Geographic Information System
IGES	International Graphics Exchange Specification - A standard format used to exchange drawing data between one application and another
ISO	International Standards Organization
MCAD	Mechanical CAD
Parametric modeling	An ability of CADD to link geometry with the calculations.
PDM	Product Data Management
Solid modeling	3D modeling that assumes the 3D objects to be solids having weight properties.

Product Selection Criteria

The following criteria may help you make a CADD program selection:

- Is CADD intended for personal use or professional? A low-end product may be accepted for personal use, but for professional use, you may want to consider a high-end product.

- Select a program compatible with the programs used by your clients and consultants. It makes sharing drawings much easier. Although you will often hear from the CADD vendors that their programs are 100% compatible with other programs, it may not be the case. Ask for a trial version of the program and confirm it.

- Review how many customization features a CADD program offers. Customization plays a major role in making CADD more productive.

- Decide whether you need to buy a brand name product or any workable CADD program. Both may provide the same capabilities, but a brand name may cost twice as much. Selecting a brand name program may give you certain advantages such as finding add-on programs and experienced users.

- Find out if the dealer offers technical support. In the beginning you may have a lot of questions about the program. Without technical support, you may have to pay hourly charges to a consultant.

- Ask if the dealer offers free or low-cost updates of the program. Most CADD programs get revised every year. You may have to pay double in four or five years to get all the updates.

- New technology advancements are taking place everyday. CADD programs are getting highly specialized to meet the needs of specific professionals. With some research you may be able to find exactly what you need and you may not have to spend a bundle.

Leading CADD Products

Today's CADD market has become highly specialized. Most CADD programs as designed to meet the needs of a specific industry. CADD companies offer different varieties of their basic program to target a specific market.

The CADD programs may be divided into the following categories:

- Architectural Engineering Construction (AEC)
- General-purpose
- Mechanical CAD
- Solid modeling
- Visualization and rendering
- Facility management
- CAD/CAM/CAE

Architectural Engineering Construction (AEC)

(All USA addresses unless otherwise noted)

Product (s)	Contact Information	Application
Allplan MiniCAD	Nemetschek AG D-81677 München Riedenburger Straße 2 Germany Phone: 0 89 / 9 27 93-0 Internet address: http://www.nemetschek.de	Allplan is a popular architectural software in Europe. Includes a number of automated features to create and manage architectural projects MiniCAD, originally developed by Diehl Graphsoft, Inc. now acquired by Nametschek AG. A popular CADD program for Macintosh (also available for Windows) is well known for its ease of use, versatility, precision drafting.
ARCHICAD	Graphisoft Inc. 235 Kansas Street Suite 200 San Francisco, CA 94103 Phone: (415) 703-9777 Internet address: http://www.graphisoft.com	Ease of use is a hallmark of this popular CAD program for architects and designers. It uses a single building file and object technology concept known as Virtual Building. ArchiCAD automatically generates all required 2D and 3D output from a single file including virtual reality tours and animations. Users work and edit directly in both 3D and 2D.

Product (s)	Contact Information	Application
ARCHITRON	BAGH Technologies 4446 Boul. St-Laurent Montreal, Quebec Canada H2W IZ5 Phone: (514) 285-1717 Internet address: http://www.architrion.com	An economically priced software for the architectural market. Includes essential 2D and 3D capabilities for building design and drafting. Includes a library of ready-made architectural features that can be instantly added to drawings. Available for Windows and Macintosh platforms.
ArchT	Eagle Point Software 4131 Westmark Drive Dubuque, IA 52002-2627 Phone: (319)556-8392 (800)678-6565 Internet address: http://www.archt.com	An add-on program for AutoCAD that enhances the architectural capabilities of AutoCAD. It allows users to automatically draw building features such as walls, doors and windows. ArchT also has the ability to maintain a record of the building features in a database that is used to prepare reports. Eagle Point Software is distributor for a number of other AutoCAD related products.
ARRIS	Sigma Design International 5221 Jackson St. Alexandria, LA 71303 Phone: (318) 449-9900 Internet address: http://www.arriscad.com	Award-winning software commonly used by architects in Europe as well as in North America. Includes a number of 2D and 3D ready-made features for architects to help them with building design and facility management. It is available for Sun Solaris and Windows platforms.
AutoCAD Architectural Desktop AutoCAD LT	Autodesk, Inc. 111 McInnis Parkway San Rafael, CA 94903 Phone: (800) 879-4233 Internet address: http://www.autodesk.com	A popular CADD program commonly used for architectural and engineering applications. The company offers a number of variations of the product for architectural, mechanical and civil engineering applications. Extremely versatile for customization. Uses Autolisp programming language, which is based on "C" and LISP. AutoCAD LT is a condensed version of AutoCAD. Intended for general-purpose drafting. It is moderately priced.
CHIEF ARCHITECT	Advanced Relational Technology, Inc. 301 N. 3rd Street Coeur d'Alene, ID 83814 Phone: (800) 482-4433 (208) 664-4204 Internet address: http://www.chiefarch.com	An architectural drafting software package commonly used by professional designers, builders, architects and remodelers. This integrated 2D and 3D package makes architectural design flexible, fast and fun. The entire spectrum of project design and development is covered in this single, stand-alone program. It includes a number of tools for developing preliminary sketch designs, 3D modeling and working drawings.

Product (s)	Contact Information	Application
MicroStation	Bentley Systems, Inc. 690 Pennsylvania Drive Exton, PA 19341 Phone: (610) 458-500 (800) BENTLEY Internet address: http://www.bentley.com	Originally developed by Intergraph, now available through Bentley Systems. It's widely used among architects and engineers. Bentley systems offers a number of engineering CADD programs for building design, geo-engineering, civil engineering, plant design, mechanical engineering, etc. They work as add-on programs with MicroStation.
DATACAD	Datacad LLC 20 Tower Lane Avon, CT 06001 Phone: (800) 394-2231 (860) 677-4004 Internet address: http://www.datacad.com	A comprehensive CADD package, which includes a number of automated features for architects. One of the first CADD programs in the market that still maintains a loyal user base. Over 280,000 users worldwide. Includes a number of advanced functions for drawing architectural elements and for preparing project reports and cost estimates. It is sold in 80 countries in 16 languages.
SoftCAD SoftCAD.3D ArchiTECH PC	SoftCAD International 1460 Washington Blvd. Suite B-205 Concord, CA 94521 Phone: (800) SOFTCAD Internet address: http://www.softcad.com	SoftCAD is great architectural software at an affordable price. Commonly used in Europe, now available in the United States. SoftCAD.3D offers comprehensive 3D drawing as well as rendering capabilities. ArchiTECH PC includes additional features such as bill of materials preparation, 3D, animation, etc.

General Purpose

Product (s)	Contact Information	Application
CADVANCE	Furukawa Information Technology (FIT), Inc. 721 N. Euclid St., Suite 303 Anaheim, CA 92801-4135 Phone: (714) 956-3171 Internet address: http://www.cadvance.com/	Moderately priced, provides all the basic drafting capabilities required to make architectural and engineering drawings. Includes basic 2D and 3D capabilities. Offers two-way database links for information management, and advanced networking capabilities. CADVANCE maintains a very extensive and loyal user following since 1982.

Product (s)	Contact Information	Application
DENEBACAD	Deneba Software 7400 S.W. 87th Ave. Miami, FL 33173 Phone: (305) 596-5644 Internet address: http://www.deneba.com	A new general-purpose drawing software, which includes 2D, 3D and basic rendering capabilities. This low-cost program has the ability to share information with most other CADD programs. Includes some fun features like Virtual Reality and 3D-stereoscopic images.
DesignCAD	Viagrafix One American Way Pryor, OK 74361 Phone: (918) 825-6700 (800) 842-4723 Internet address: http://www.designcad.com/	A basic drafting program that includes an integrated 2D and 3D modes for drafting. This easy to learn and use program offers most of the features of leading CAD programs at an affordable price. It includes basic capabilities for 3D modeling, solid modeling, animation, networking and web publishing.
DYNACADD	Ditek Software Corp. 60 West Wilmont Street Richmond Hill, Ontario Canada L4B 1M6 Phone: (905) 771-8000 Internet address: http://www.ditek.com	A general-purpose 2D and 3D software recommended for personal use. Its intuitive interface makes it easy to learn and use. It includes basic editing and presentation tools such as scanned image support. Its built-in symbol library allows you to add many common shapes to drawings.
EasyCAD FastCAD	Evolution Computing 437 S 48th St., Suite 106 Tempe, AZ 85281-9936 Phone: (800) 874-4028 Internet address: http://www.fastcad.com	EasyCAD is a low-cost 2D CADD program intended for basic drawing. It is intended for personal use. FastCAD offers comprehensive 2D drawing and editing features. This easy to use software is also recommended for personal use.
FELIXCAD	FCAD Software, Inc. 2105 Ridgerock Place West Bank, BC Canada V4T 1S7 Phone: (800) 668-2320 Internet address: http://www.fcad.com	Originally developed in Germany, FlexiCAD has gained popularity in Europe, and is now introduced in the United States. It's considered an AutoCAD "work-alike"; meaning it recognizes most of the commands used in AutoCAD and uses the same methodology. Affordably priced.

Product (s)	Contact Information	Application
POWERCAD	Engineered Software 615 Guilford Jamestown Rd. P.O.Box. 18344 Greensboro, NC 27419-8344 Phone: (336) 299-4843 Internet address: http://www.engsw.com	A popular CADD program among Macintosh users. Production oriented software used to prepare architectural and engineering or any general-purpose drawings. Affordably priced, includes all the basic capabilities such as layers, symbols, hatch patterns, dimensioning, etc.
Smart Sketch	Intergraph Corporation 1 Madison Industrial Park Huntsville, AL 35824 Phone: (800) 692-8069 Internet address: http://www.intergraph.com	Intergraph has developed a number of advanced CADD solutions. Smart Sketch happens to be a very basic, general-purpose drawing software. It is easy to learn and use and can be used to make quick presentations. The drawings can be easily exported into other applications. Includes web-publishing capabilities.
VDRAFT	SoftSource 301 West Holly Street Bellingham, WA 98225 Phone: (360) 676-0999 Internet address: http://www.softsource.com	One of a kind program that has the capability to work directly with AutoCAD and DXF drawings in their native format without translation. It uses the same technology built into the core of AutoCAD. This 2D drafting program that is easy to use, fast and affordable. It is known to be 100% compatible with AutoCAD. However, it does not include advanced capabilities of AutoCAD.
VISIO TECHNICAL	Visio Corp. 520 Pike Street, Suite 1800 Seattle, WA 98101 Phone: (206) 521-4500 Internet address: http://www.visio.com	A general-purpose 2D software that can be used for making technical illustrations. Specifically designed to make schematic diagrams that are linked with a database. Commonly used to prepare flow diagrams and analytical charts often required for project development.

Visualization and Rendering

Product (s)	Contact Information	Application
AccuRender	Robert McNeel & Associates 3670 Woodland Park, Ave. N Seattle, WA 98103 Phone: (206) 545-7000 Internet address: http://www.accurender.com/	A popular rendering software that works inside AutoCAD. It uses raytracing and radiosity technologies to create high quality, still and animated images. It allows you to apply hundreds of materials, textures, colors and lights available in the library. Includes a number of tools to analyze shades, shadows and reflections.

Product (s)	Contact Information	Application
3D Studio MAX 3D Studio VIZ LIGHTSCAPE	Autodesk, Inc. 111 McInnis Parkway San Rafael, CA 94903 Phone: (800) 879-4233 Internet address: http://www.autodesk.com Note: 3D Studio MAX and 3D Studio VIZ is distributed through Kinetix – a division of Autodesk	3D Studio MAX is specifically known for its animation capabilities. It uses object-oriented approach for animation that can animate any rendered image. 3D Studio VIZ is a comprehensive rendering program. It is a complex program to learn, but the benefits are worth the effort. Can produce photo-realistic renderings required for product design. Lightscape is another rendering software known for its lighting and material effects. Commonly used by interior designers.
Art*lantis	ABVENT,Inc. 235 Kansas Street Suite 203 San Francisco, CA 94103 Phone: (800) 452-9241 Internet address: http://www.artlantis.com/	A simple to use rendering software that includes most of the rendering capabilities at an affordable price. It can import 3D models created in different programs and add lighting, textures, materials and coloring effects. Includes basic features for animation and virtual reality that are easy to apply.
FormZ	Autodessys Inc. 2011 Riverside Drive Columbus, Ohio 43221 Phone: (614) 488-8838 Internet address: http://www.formz.com	An excellent 3D and rendering software that can quickly create different 3D shapes including sculptured surfaces. Intended for artists and architects. The rendering capabilities of FormZ are well known in the industry and many professionals use it to create 3D models as well as render models created with other programs.
Virtus	Virtus Corporation 114 MacKenan Drive Suite 100 Cary, NC 27511 Phone: (919)467-9700 Internet address: http://www.virtus.com	Vitrus offers a number of products for the CAD visualization industry. They are intended for various sectors of the market, including architecture, mechanical design, product design, interior design, film and entertainment industry. It includes powerful presentation tools for multimedia presentations.

Facility Management CADD

Product (s)	Contact Information	Application
APERTURE	Aperture Technologies, Inc. 9 Riverbend Drive South Stamford, CT 06907 Phone: (203) 357-0800 Internet address: http://www.aperture.com	A platform for creating visual facility management applications. Noted for its ease of use and customization. Thousands of architects and facility managers around the world use it to track space, personnel, furniture, equipment, etc. Includes a large number of pre-defined reports that can be used for dynamic presentations. Its database is very flexible and can easily access information in other databases as well as referencing existing CAD files.
ARCHIBUS	Archibus, Inc. 100 Franklin Street Boston, MA 02110 Phone: (617) 338-1011 Internet address: http://www.archibus.com	An add-on program to AutoCAD for facility management applications. It has the largest market share in the facility management software market. Includes a number of automated features to place design elements such as furniture, equipment, etc., in a database. This database can be used to prepare customized reports and to make instant presentations.
DRAWBASE	Graphisoft, Inc. 235 Kansas Street Suite 200 San Francisco, CA 94103 Phone: (415) 703-9777 Internet address: http://www.graphisoft.com	A comprehensive facility management software. It has basic drawing capabilities, but its main function is to prepare schedules, reports and space analysis diagrams. It can use existing CADD drawings created by other CADD programs and add intelligent attributes to them. These attributes are stored in a database that is used to prepare reports. Commonly used by government and public agencies.

Mechanical CADD

Product (s)	Contact Information	Application
CADKEY	Baystate Technologies 33 Boston Post Road West MA 01752 Phone: (508) 229-2020 Internet address: http://www.baystate.com	A very popular CADD program among mechanical engineers. Over 235,000 users worldwide. Offers comprehensive 2D drafting and 3D modeling capabilities at an affordable price. Includes a number of advanced features for drawing, editing, rendering, solid modeling and animation.

Product (s)	Contact Information	Application
CADMAX	Cadmax Corp. 258 Village Square Village of Cross Keys Baltimore, MD 21210 Phone: (800) CADMAX-1 Internet address: http://www.cadmax.com	A highly productive, moderately priced mechanical CADD program, which includes 2D, 3D and rendering features. It includes a number of solid modeling features, which makes mechanical design flexible, fast and fun. With CADMAX Solid Mater you can perform parametric, feature-based solid modeling and free-form surface modeling.
AutoCAD Mechanical Desktop	Autodesk, Inc. 111 McInnis Parkway San Rafael, CA 94903 Phone: (800) 879-4233 Internet address: http://www.autodesk.com	Mechanical Desktop is an extension of AutoCAD that includes specific functions for mechanical engineering. Introduced only a few years ago, it created a niche for itself very quickly. Offers comprehensive features for mechanical designers to create, edit and manage large assemblies. It includes a comprehensive library of mechanical parts that can be instantly added to drawings.
VELLUM	Ashlar, Inc. 12731 Research Blvd. Building A Austin, TX 78759 Phone: (800) 877-2745 (512) 250-2186 Internet address: http://www.ashlar.com/	A family of 2D and 3D wireframe and 3D surface and solid modeling products popular among industrial designers and mechanical engineers. Easy to learn and use software that incorporates unique user interface and integrates 2D drawings, wire-frame models, surface models and solid models. Available for Windows and Macintosh platforms.

Solid Modeling   (See CAD/CAM/CAE section for more products in this category.)

Product (s)	Contact Information	Application
Helix Design System	Microcadam, Inc. 2255 N. Ontario St., Suite 300 Burbank, CA 91504 Phone: (800) 255-5710 Internet address: http://www.microcadam.com	The Helix Design System is a full-function mechanical CAD/CAM system. It combines high productivity design/drafting with hybrid parametric and solid modeling. The two base modules provide solid modeling and drafting capabilities. There are additional modules available for viewing, rendering, data management and CAM.
IronCAD	Visionary Design Systems 2790 Walsh Avenue Santa Clara, CA 95051 Phone: (800) 339-7304 Internet address: http://www.ironcad.com/	A mechanical engineering oriented solid modeling program. First released in 1998, has received a number of favorable reviews from professionals. It provides a highly productive environment for design engineers. Uses advanced technology to form complex assemblies and to design individual parts within an assembly.

Product (s)	Contact Information	Application
SOLIDWORKS	Dassault Systems U.S.A. 300 Baker Avenue Ext. Concord, MA 01742 Phone: (978) 371-5000 Internet address: http://www.solidworks.com	A comprehensive solid modeling program widely used by mechanical engineers. Can create renderings, animation and simulations. It has a user-friendly interface that includes a number of tools to create and manage complex assemblies.

CAD/CAM/CAE

Product (s)	Contact Information	Application
CADRA	SofTech, Inc. 2 Highwood Drive Tewksbury, MA 01876 Phone: (978) 640-6222 Internet address: http://www.softech.com/	An integrated software for CAD-CAM applications. It includes detail drafting, 3D modeling, solid modeling, machine tool programming, project information management, etc. Designed for large manufacturing environments. Besides the United States, it has a large market in Europe and Asia. Previously available only for UNIX systems now available for Windows platforms as well.
CATIA-CADAM	IBM USA Marketing Response Line 1507 LBJ Freeway Dallas, TX 75234 USA Phone: (972) 280-2968 Internet address: http://www.ibm.com	CATIA-CADAM is a fully integrated CAD-CAM package that supports many applications such as drafting, design, spreadsheets, engineering analysis, product data management and manufacturing. It runs on Windows based PCs, minicomputers and mainframes. A high-end product intended for medium and large organizations.
I-DEAS	Structural Dynamics Research Corp. (SRDC) 2000 Eastman Drive Milford, OH 45150 Phone: (513) 576-2400 Internet address: http://www.sdrc.com	One of the largest developers of mechanical CAD and engineering solutions. I-IDEAS is an integrated package for mechanical design engineering that includes solid modeling, computer-aided manufacturing capabilities, engineering analysis and product data management. A number of other products and offered for specific engineering applications.

Product (s)	Contact Information	Application
Pro/Engineer CADDS MEDUSA	Parametric Technology Corporation (PTC) 128 Technology Drive Waltham, MA 02154 Phone: (781) 398-5000 Internet address: http://www.ptc.com PTC has more than 100 service centers all over the world.	Pro/Engineer is highly productive software for CAD, CAM and CAE. A well accepted program in the mechanical industry. PTC offers comprehensive e-business solutions for collaborative product development. CADDS is an integrated package that includes product design, drafting, engineering analysis and manufacturing modules. MEDUSA is a mechanical design software, which provides a number of automated features for mechanical designers.
Unigraphics Solid Edge	Unigraphics Solutions 13736 Riverport Drive Maryland Heights, MO 63043 Phone: (314) 344-5900 (800) DIAL-UGS Unigraphics has more than 100 offices worldwide. Internet address: http://www.ugsolutions.com	One of the largest developers of MCAD/CAM/CAE/PDM integrated software. Unigraphics includes a number of modules for product design, drafting, 3D solid modeling, engineering analysis and project management and CAM. Used by a number or large corporation to manufacture cars, airplanes, medical implant devices and machine tools. Solid Edge is a mid-range CAD software for mechanical design, drafting, solid modeling and product assembly.

Important CADD Resources on the Internet

CADD resources available on the Internet are vast. There are more than 100,000 web sites established for CADD-related products and services. If you search the web for the words CAD or CADD, it will list thousands of sites within seconds. You can spend a lifetime researching CADD using the Internet. The following are some important resources on the Internet:

Note: You can access all the Internet sites listed here through a web site dedicated to this book at http://www.caddprimer.com/.

Organizations associated with CADD

Description	Internet address
Association for Computer Aided Design in Architecture (ACADIA)	http://www.acadia.org/
Facility Information Council (FIC) of National Institute of Building Sciences (NIBS): An organization involved in developing U.S. national CAD standards.	http://nationalcadstandard.org/ http://www.nibs.org/
CAD Society	http://www.cadsociety.org/
American Design and Drafting Association (ADDA)	http://www.adda.org/
American Society of Mechanical Engineers (ASME)	http://www.asme.org/ (Search for word "CAD")
Institute of Electrical & Electronics Engineers (IEEE)	http://gopher.ieee.org/ (Search for word "CAD")
American Institute of Architects (AIA)	http://www.aiaonline.com/ (Search for word "CAD")
Computer Aided Architectural Design Research In Asia (CAADRIA)	http://www.caadria.org/
Education in Computer Aided Architectural Design in Europe (ECAADE)	http://www.ecaade.org/
CADD/GIS Technology Center: A multi-agency vehicle to coordinate CADD/GIS standards used by US Department of Defense and other government agencies.	http://tsc.wes.army.mil/

CADD magazines and journals

Description	Internet address
CADENCE: A leading CADD magazine focusing on the CADD industry.	http://www.cadence-mag.com/
CADSYSTEMS: A leading CADD magazine focusing on the CAAD industry. Available for free in Canada.	http://www.cadsystems.com/
CADALYST: A popular magazine focusing on AutoCAD.	http://www.cadonline.com
An electronic CADD magazine (e-zine) focusing on the CADD industry news. You can subscribe this weekly e-zine free of charge.	http://www.upfrontezine.com/
Joint CAD Journal: Engineering magazine from Russia	http://sungraph.jinr.dubna.su/jcj/
TCAD Journal: The Journal of Technology, Computer Aided Design.	http://www.ieee.org/journal/tcad/

Description	Internet address
CAD/CAM Publishing: books, magazines, industry links	http://www.cadcamnet.com/
CAD User Online: Australian/ Neuziland CAD magazine	http://www.caduser.com.au/

CADD Directories and Gateways

Description	Internet address
3zone: A comprehensive database of CADD companies, publications and resources	http://www.3zone.com/
CAD baseline URL database: Allows you to search products in a specific category	http://www.basline.com/basline/cadURLs.htm/
CAD Forum: CADD news, employment, companies, usergroups, dictionary	http://www.cad-forum.com
CAD on the Web: A database of CADD products and services	http://www.cadontheweb.com/
CAD open directory: Maintains a list of CADD products in different categories	http://dmoz.org/computers/cad/
Product Information Retrieval System (PIRS) for construction & design professionals	http://www.insa.com/
TenLinks: A comprehensive directory of CADD products	http://www.tenlinks.com/

Important CADD Resources

Description	Internet address
AEC Info. Center: architecture, engineering, building construction links	http://www.aecinfo.com/ (Search for word "CAD")
Architectural CADD: Ratings and reviews	http://www.architecturalcadd.com/
CAD Depot: CADD software resource	http://www.caddepot.com/
CAD Info net: CADD news, reviews and links	http://www.cadinfo.net/
CAD Source International: Australia	http://www.cadsource.com.au/
Daratech, Inc.: Ranking of CADD software	http://www.daratech.com/
The CAD Place: Comprehensive lists of CADD products and services	http://www.cadplace.cjb.net/

Important CADD Links

Description	Internet address
CADD rating guide	http://www.cadratingguide.com/
Technical drawing/drafting resources on the Internet	http://www.gmi.edu/official/acad/mech-eng/drafting.htm

Description	Internet address
Technical drawing/drafting resources on the Internet	http://www.gmi.edu/official/acad/mech-eng/drafting.htm
PC and CAD encyclopedia on the web and links	http://www.pcwebopaedia.com/CAD_CAM.htm
CAD-CAM & graphics sites around the world	http://www.flash.net/~cdhb/Cadlinks2.htm
CAD home page: U.S. Department of Energy	http://www-cad.fnal.gov/

CADD vendors

Description	Internet address
Proven Solutions, Inc.: Links to over 480 hardware and software manufacturers.	http://www.proven-solutions.com/
CAD Studio on-line: CADD links	http://www.cadstudio.cz/
CADD links and symbol libraries	http://www.cadeasy.com/
Design Technology Warehouse	http://www-cad.eecs.berkeley.edu/Software/software.html
CAD information sources and manufacturers	http://www.compinfo.co.uk/tpcad.htm
The CAD Shack: CADD industry links	http://www.cadshack.com/
CAD WIRE: CAD/CAM training and support	http://www.cadwire.com/

Important note:

The information on the World Wide Web is constantly being updated. If you find that you cannot access an Internet address listed here, the developer of that site may have moved that page somewhere else. You can log on to a web site dedicated to this book http://www.caddprimer.com/ to receive the most current information.

If you have any comments or need more information, E-mail info@caddprimer.com

Index